Introduction

I know how hard it is to care for a loved one with [dementia. My mum was] diagnosed with early onset frontotemporal dementia in her fifties. After her diagnosis my siblings and I cared for her for five years, but at times, I felt completely overwhelmed by what I'd taken on and often struggled to find the information, support or advice I needed.

However, I now realise that although I felt alone, I wasn't, because there is a silent army of carers doing exactly what I did and experiencing the same practical challenges. They, like me, simply muddle through as best they can, often learning at the point of crisis and usually feeling a whole complex range of emotions, from worry, frustration, and guilt, to relief and even joy when things go well.

The dementia journey is full of challenges. I founded www.unforgettable.org to make those challenges a bit easier to cope with and that's why we've compiled this book. It's the book I wish I'd had. We hope it will help you with all aspects of daily life, to offer you some new ideas based on experience, and to remind you that you're doing a great job under very difficult circumstances.

Remember, you aren't alone.

James

James Ashwell, Founder, Unforgettable.org

Chapter 1: The Basics

If your loved one has a good daily routine, a healthy diet and gets enough rest and sleep, their life — and yours — will be much more enjoyable. Here's how to make it happen.

Creating a Plan

A daily routine won't only help your loved one feel safe and secure, it will also help you feel as if you're achieving something — however small — each day. If the person you're caring for is only mildly affected by dementia, planning activities might be quite straightforward, but it will probably get tougher. The more practice you have at keeping to a routine and knowing what's achievable, the better.

Could this be you?

You're doing your best to make sure your loved one is cared for properly but;

1. Some days seem to fly by without you getting anything done.

2. Other days go really slowly and you worry about them getting bored.

3. Whatever kind of day it is, you never have a minute to yourself.

Creating a simple structure to each day could help you avoid these common pitfalls — and maybe even enjoy life a little more! And don't worry, it isn't hard and it won't take long to do.

What is a daily care plan?

A daily care plan is a written or visual description of activities and events taking place each day. The aim of a care plan is to ensure that the person with dementia has all their basic needs taken care of, gets as much pleasure and stimulation as possible from each day and can see for themselves what each day has in store.

How do I make a daily care plan?

You can use a paper template or an activity board. It can be written out in the style of a timetable, or it can be created on an activity board using visual prompts, pictures and cards for each activity.

Why bother?

Routine works

Many people living with dementia feel as though they're losing control of their lives, which can be frightening. If you're feeling lost and confused it can help to know that certain daily events will always happen at a certain time. Besides, most people like to have a routine, and a person with dementia is no exception.

It anchors each day

Generally speaking, we all function best if we have a regular bedtime, get up at around the same time each day and eat regular meals. So whenever possible try to stick to the same times. It's a simple way to provide a focus and structure to the day.

It keeps everyone informed

The person with dementia simply has to look at the plan to know what's happening next, and other carers, family or friends can also see what's happened earlier in the day and avoid repeating the same activity or meal.

Three questions to ask before you make your plan

1. What time did they used to like going to bed or getting up?

If they liked to have a bath in the evening and a main meal at lunchtime, try to accommodate that whenever you can because it will help them to feel calm, which in turn will help you.

2. What did they used to like doing before?

They might not be able to do the crossword anymore or knit an Aran jumper but maybe they can still read the newspaper or knit a scarf? Remember, it doesn't matter how well they do each activity, what counts is that they've enjoyed the process.

3. What activities could you enjoy together?

Your lives have undoubtedly changed since the diagnosis but that doesn't mean you can't still enjoy each other's company. For example, introduce a once-a-week movie night when you eat popcorn and watch a favourite film together.

Do

Be realistic

Keep your plan as simple as possible, it's the quality of each day that matters, not the quantity of activities and tasks you manage to cram in.

Be flexible

The routine is there to help you, not to control you. If something unexpected comes up, it's okay to be spontaneous.

Don't

Forget about you

Scheduling in time for yourself each day isn't selfish, it's vital for your mental health. Even if it's just 20 minutes having a cup of tea on your own, or watching your favourite soap, make sure you take it.

A typical daily care plan

Morning

Wake up, help with washing and dressing if necessary

Prepare and eat a healthy breakfast

Morning activity — gardening, cooking, a craft project

Coffee and newspapers

Quiet time to relax or take a nap

Afternoon

Prepare lunch and eat

Reminiscence — look at photos together, listen to favourite music or do some life story work

Activity – household chores

Take a break

Prepare evening meal

Evening

Watch TV, play a card game, run a bath

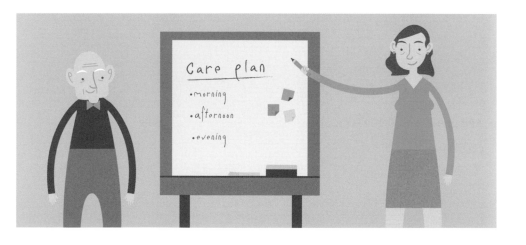

 Good to know

There are more social groups and activities for people with dementia than ever before. From singing and dancing, to yoga and reminiscence therapy, so there's no need for anyone to sit at home all day and be bored. Getting out and about is good for you and the person you're caring for.

Eating Healthily

It can be very worrying to watch someone you love not eating properly, but sadly dementia can often affect the appetite. Find out how to help them eat healthier and stay well.

Could this be you?

You know that a nutritious diet will help the person you're caring for stay stronger for longer, and you make a big effort to provide meals and drinks they like, but

- They don't want to eat it — in fact they don't want to eat much at all.
- They've developed a sweet tooth and just want cakes, biscuits and chocolate.
- They forget to drink the endless cups of tea you make.

Try not to panic or take it personally. Instead, look at the tips below — it might be easier than you think to make some positive changes.

It's not all about the food

Creating a calm, relaxing environment is just as important as the food on their plate. Turn off the TV and don't bother with background music. Set the table nicely — better still, ask them to help you — but keep it simple. Table arrangements, flowers or candles could confuse them. Make sure that plates, place mats and table clothes are in contrasting colours, otherwise visual spatial difficulties might mean they have trouble distinguishing them. And most importantly, sit down and eat with them (unless they really do prefer eating alone).

Keep it small

There's nothing worse than being presented with a seemingly massive meal when you don't feel hungry. Since people with dementia often lose their appetite, it's likely that they'll be much happier with a smaller portion than they used to eat. Try serving it on a smaller plate, or give them half as much and save the rest for later.

Keep it balanced

Offer vegetables they like, lean meats and whole grains whenever possible. Limit salt, butter and fatty cuts of meat. Keeping healthy will provide energy and can reduce the risk of illness. Try making a fruit salad, keep it in the fridge and serve up in tiny amounts throughout the day so they've got something to nibble on.

Keep it tasty

People with dementia often find their sense of taste and smell declines — food that used to taste and smell good before, no longer does. However, that might mean they develop a liking for something different, so don't be afraid to experiment. Spices and herbs with stronger flavours might go down much better than you imagine.

If they're losing weight and you're getting really worried, try adding a spoonful of honey or sugar. Sweet food might be more appealing than savoury. If they're putting weight on, but have developed a sweet tooth, try to choose natural sugars such as fruit.

You may want to try a sensory stimulator. This is a product designed to stimulate the appetite of a person with dementia by releasing authentic smells of food cooking. The smell of breakfast, lunch or dinner can serve as a meal time prompt and also help create a homely environment.

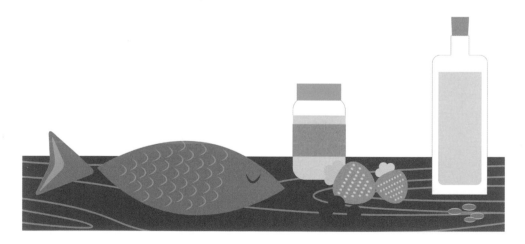

Keep it warm

It might take them longer to eat a meal than it used to and a cold dinner can quickly become unappetizing. Give the food a quick blast in the microwave or think about buying a keep-warm plate, but always check it's not too hot before serving again.

Keep it easy

As the illness progresses cutlery might become quite difficult to manage but it's important to help your loved one retain as much independence as possible.

Serve up snacks and meals that are easy to eat with fingers. For example, meatballs, fish fingers, chunky chips, and cooked veg such as carrot sticks and asparagus. Or provide ergonomic cutlery, which makes it easier to pick up food. Remember, you don't have to stick to three meals a day. Five or six mini meals served at regular intervals might be more manageable.

Plates and crockery specially designed for people with dementia are also useful. Brightly coloured crockery, anti-tipping cups with extended handles and rimmed bowls can all help make eating as easy as possible for those with cognitive or motor impairments.

 Did you know?

A study by Boston University revealed that a person with dementia can eat 24 per cent more food, and drink 84 per cent more liquid if their plates and cups are red or blue.

Keep it personal

Favourite foods can have a powerful effect on our mood so try to make sure that treats are given as often as possible, and that they're given a choice whenever possible. If it's too difficult for them to tell you their choice, try using menu cards or show them pictures of their favourite meals from recipe books.

For someone with dementia who's feeling lost, frightened or confused, a favourite treat that you know they like, such as a hot buttered tea cake, or a plate of cheese and biscuits, won't only cheer them up, it might also help them to feel calmer and safer.

Food can also be a very powerful tool for reminiscence — perhaps they loved a bowl of Angel Delight when they were younger? This could be an ideal treat and way to get them chatting about the past.

Keep up their drinks

Forgetting to drink is a really common problem and since dehydration can also cause confusion (as well as other health concerns such as urinary tract infections and constipation) it's important to keep a careful watch on how much they're actually drinking.

Try sitting down with them to drink a cup of tea or coffee, even if it means leaving the washing up or ironing. Give yourself a break! If you feel guilty remind yourself that this is very important for your loved one's health.

Serve juices and cold drinks in brightly coloured glasses or beakers and put it in their hand, not on a table next to them. Use cups that are anti-spill if necessary.

Keep calm

If none of this seems to work, don't give up, just keep going. You can only do your best. If your efforts don't pay off today, they might tomorrow...

 Good to know

Try going for a walk or just getting outside in the fresh air before eating a meal. The activity and a change of scenery might help stimulate a poor appetite.

Staying Safe

You probably dread the thought of the person you're caring for having an accident at home. Find out how to reduce the risks and keep everyone safe.

Could this be you?

Your loved one is determined to remain independent for as long as possible, but although they seem to be coping quite well around the home, you can't help thinking that they might hurt or injure themselves.

Try not to worry. It's true that older people are more vulnerable to accidents at home, particularly if they're frail and becoming increasingly confused, however there are steps you can take to protect them.

Eight questions to ask yourself

Are they losing…

- Strength — Are previously simple tasks, such as carrying a tea pot or lifting a mug proving too strenuous? Are they often spilling drinks?
- Balance — Do they seem unsteady when they get up from a bed or chair?
- Coordination — Is it a struggle to use a tin opener, tie shoes or make a sandwich?
- Confidence — Are they becoming tense and anxious about walking downstairs, turning on a cooker or boiling a kettle?

Are they using…

- A kettle they've had for years?
- Crockery or household items that are too heavy?
- Matches, lighters or candles?
- The wrong equipment for the task? For example, using a sharp knife to spread butter, or pouring hot water into a wine glass?

If you've answered 'yes' to some of these questions, you might find the tips below useful.

11 ways to prevent accidents at home

- Most accidents in the home happen on stairs or in the kitchen so make sure each of these areas are as dementia-friendly as possible.

- Generally speaking, loose-fitting carpets, low-lighting and clutter should be avoided whenever possible since they can increase the possibility of a person with dementia tripping, slipping or having a nasty fall.

- Badly fitted footwear, particularly worn-out slippers, can also make trips and falls more likely, so replace any that have seen better days.

- Keep everyday items in easy reach so they aren't tempted to climb or stretch too far for a plate or mug.

- Consider swapping heavier, breakable crockery for lighter dementia-friendly versions and replace an old, heavy kettle with a long lead, for a cordless lighter version.

- Make sure medication, household cleaners, matches and candles are kept under lock and key.

- Be realistic — accidents might still happen but try to stay calm and keep it in perspective. Broken crockery can be replaced, spills can be wiped up.

- Make sure they have easy access to a dust-pan and brush (a long-handled pan and broom may be better if they struggle to kneel or bend) so that broken items can be easily cleared away.

- Keep a small fire extinguisher or fire blanket in an obvious place in the kitchen and make sure there is a smoke alarm and carbon monoxide detector (with regularly changed batteries) in the kitchen.

- Have a well-stocked first aid kit ready and waiting in case anything should happen. It should include plasters, antiseptic cream, bandages, sterile dressings and distilled water.

- Encourage independence. Your instinct may be to wrap them in cotton wool, but once you've taken a few sensible precautions it's probably wiser to let a person with dementia continue doing simple tasks for themselves. Retaining a sense of independence won't only boost their confidence, it could bring enjoyment and give meaning and purpose to life.

Facts about fires: Radiators, electric fires, cookers, and kettles can cause everything from minor scalds to serious injuries for elderly people. In fact, they're nearly five times more likely to suffer a fatal injury from a burn or scald than someone who is younger, often because they're already frail or in poor health.

Sleeping Well

Many people living with dementia have trouble getting to sleep, or wake up often during the night. Whilst it's true that older people generally need less sleep than they used to, this doesn't mean that they — or you — have to suffer endless nights of broken sleep.

Here's 13 ways to encourage the person you care for to sleep.

Daytime

Achieving good sleep means planning ahead and making sure that your daytime routine includes stimulating activity and a nap if necessary.

1. Get outside twice a day.

Dementia can disturb the body clock which is why some people with dementia get day and night mixed up. Outdoor light in the morning and early evening can help to regulate the body clock. Try combining it with a little exercise, too, such as a walk in the park, as physical tiredness tends to promote better sleep in most people.

2. If they need a nap, make it before lunch not after.

A daytime nap isn't necessarily wrong, many older people like to nap and without one they may become over tired, irritable and unable to sleep at night. However, try to make sure their nap happens sooner in the day (before 1 pm) rather than in the afternoon.

3. Watch what they're drinking.

It's very important that people with dementia drink plenty of fluids throughout the day (dehydration can cause more confusion and illnesses such as urinary tract infections) but try to limit tea and coffee after around 5pm as too much caffeine could keep them wide awake at night. Generally speaking, aim to give most of their daily fluid intake during the day and early evening, not in the couple of hours leading up to bed, as this can make trips to the bathroom in the middle of the night far more likely.

Evening

This is when you can start to focus on rest and relaxation. The calmer a person with dementia is feeling in the evening, the better chance they have of sleeping well.

4. Lighten the mood with music or feel-good TV.

A favourite comedy show or CD is a great way to help them relax and boost their mood. Avoid discussing anything which might be potentially upsetting or difficult at this time, too. Focus on good memories and positive conversation.

5. Run a bath.

This is the perfect time to suggest a relaxing soak in the bath. If they're agreeable, try adding a few drops of aromatherapy essential oils (lavender and camomile are very relaxing).

6. A massage is a great way to unwind before bed.

Offer to pamper them with a shoulder massage, or a hand and foot massage.
Don't underestimate the power of human touch, it can be extremely soothing and comforting.

Bedtime

7. Spend a little time thinking about how they used to prepare themselves for bed before they were diagnosed with dementia.

Most people have roughly the same bedtime routine for many years, so what was theirs? For example, did they always drink a cup of hot chocolate and listen to Radio 4 in bed? Or read a thriller? Try to replicate this routine as far as possible now. The more familiar it feels, the better. A routine they recognise can help a person with dementia feel secure, particularly if they're no longer living in their own home.

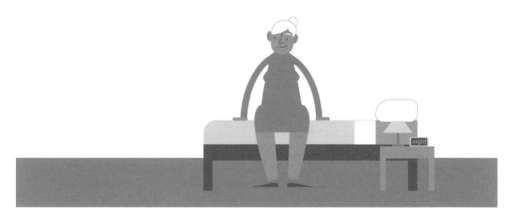

The Bedroom

It's important that the bedroom is a comfortable, safe and pleasant environment.

8. Get the basics right.

Are the curtains heavy enough to stop light getting in? If not, could you add black out lining or some blackout blinds to them? Is the temperature comfortable? If it's too hot or cold the person you're caring for won't be very comfortable and is likely to keep waking up. The best temperature is around 18°C.

9. Put daytime clothes out of sight.

If they can see them they might think it's time to get up. Cover up mirrors — people with dementia are sometimes unable to recognise their own reflection. Imagine how scary it would be to suddenly see a stranger in your bedroom in the night?

10. Pay attention to their bedside table.

For example, if it contains a dementia clock, a familiar photograph or favourite ornament, and a night light or lamp, then it will help the person you're caring for to feel safer and less confused if they wake during the night.

During the night

If, despite everything you've done, they still keep waking at night, try not to feel despondent. Remember, this is a common symptom of dementia — around 40 per cent of people will suffer sleep disruption.

11. Look at other possible causes of night time waking and wandering.

Medication or other health issues could be playing a part so turn to Chapter Four to get more information.

12. Focus on increasing their comfort if they're awake at night.

For example, leave a photograph album or picture book next to a bedside lamp.

13. Consider ways to minimise potential safety risks.

For example, would a bed monitor or stairgate at the top of the stairs stop you from worrying about them having a nasty accident? If you can't stop them wandering at night, you can at least make sure they're safe so you can get some much needed sleep yourself.

Chapter 2: Every day struggles

Helping a person with dementia to live each day to the best of their ability might feel like running an obstacle race. Finding ways to overcome the daily, sometimes hourly, challenges and barriers will test you both physically and mentally. But the rewards when you succeed can also be very worthwhile. So hold on and get ready for a bumpy ride!

Three common challenges — and how to cope with them

1. Wandering and getting lost

It's common for people with dementia to wander off on their own, leaving the person caring for them in an acute state of anxiety. Here's how to minimize the risks of wandering:

Why does it happen?

Imagine feeling disorientated or frightened by your surroundings. Chances are you'd probably want to get away from the environment which is making you feel so confused? When a person with dementia has the urge to 'wander' it's often because they're feeling something similar. Maybe they don't recognise the bedroom they've just woken up in, or the armchair they're sitting in. Maybe they're panicking because they think they're going to be late for work, or have forgotten to buy food for dinner.

Whatever the reason, if they feel the need to get up and go out, it can be difficult — but not impossible — to persuade them otherwise. Here's what to do:

Work out the reason

Are they feeling restless? Do you need to help them fight boredom? Is there a pattern to their restlessness? For example, could it be the time of day? Sundowning can increase restlessness and agitation (see Chapter Four). Or is there a more obvious reason? For example, perhaps they're trying to find a loo or they're hungry and want to buy something to eat?

Talk calmly

Keep reminding them where they are and why they're here. If they're worried about something in particular, reassure them as much as you can. You'll find ideas about dealing with awkward questions in Chapter Three.

Keep busy

A bit of physical activity, or a favourite hobby to make them feel connected and engaged might be all that's needed to reduce your loved one's desire to wander. Besides, if they've had a stimulating, active day, they're more likely to enjoy returning home, than if they've been stuck inside all day.

Develop a good bedtime routine

Dementia can cause sleep disturbance. If the person you're caring for doesn't seem to be getting enough sleep, they could be feeling even more restless and disorientated. Improving their sleep routine can reduce insomnia and may also help prevent night-time wandering.

Take a trip down memory lane

If their desire to wander seems to have been triggered by something from the past, it might help to sit down and talk about the memory together. For example, many people with dementia say 'I want to go home' when they really mean somewhere they used to live a long time ago. Looking at photos and recalling happy memories may reduce their need to 'go home.'

If none of this works consider these practical tips:

1. Remove triggers.

Keep coats, umbrellas, walking shoes, bags, purses, and door and car keys out of sight.

2. Camouflage the front door.

Cover it with a curtain or paint it the same colour as the surrounding wall. You could also put a dark rug in front of it. To someone with dementia, this may look like a hole in the floor so they won't try to cross it. Try putting a sign above the door saying 'Stop,' or 'Do not Enter.'

3. Secure doors and windows.

If you're at home but can't be watching them constantly, make sure window locks are fastened and doors are secured. You could also consider an alarm or monitor which would alert you if they do still decide to go out.

If they are absolutely determined to go out, you can't always stop them.

Instead, try to make sure:

4. They always carry identification

Even if you have to sew a name tag and phone number into their clothes.

5. Neighbours and people living nearby have been warned and know to call you if they see your loved one walking on their own.

6. Consider a tracking device

There are lots to choose from and it could save you a lot of stress and heartache.

If all else fails...

7. Could you go with them?

It may be inconvenient but sometimes accompanying them on a trip out is the simplest way to ensure they stay safe and don't get lost. You may find that they're ready to come home within about 15 minutes...and you could spend a lot longer trying to persuade them not to go out.

8. Be prepared for the worst.

If they do get lost, make sure you have phone numbers to hand for people who need to know what's happened — from neighbours and relatives to emergency services or community police. Try adding them to your mobile contacts and have a recent photo of the person with dementia and a list of places they may have gone.

Try not to worry

Around 60 per cent of people with dementia are prone to wandering, but the vast majority of them remain safe.

2. Repetitive Behaviour

Watching a loved one with dementia either do or say the same thing over and over again can test the patience of the most laid-back carer and make an already difficult day go rapidly downhill.

Could this be you?

You've always considered yourself a calm, patient, loving person and you find caring for someone with dementia very rewarding, but...

- They keep asking you the same question, or saying the same word or phrase, over and over again.
- They've developed some really annoying gestures or mannerisms which they do continually.
- They insist on walking up and down, or round in circles, for no apparent reason.

Repetitive behaviour is, sadly, quite a common symptom of dementia and although it may seem quite trivial, it can be extremely irritating and cause a lot of tension between you and the person you're caring for.

Remember

It isn't deliberate

Even though repetitive behaviour might be driving you potty, it's rarely intentionally designed to provoke you, even if your relationship with your loved one has been strained and tested by the illness.

It isn't dangerous

Repetitive behaviour rarely causes any harm to the person with dementia, so try not to worry too much about it and instead look for ways to cope with it (see below).

Three common causes of repetitive behaviour

1. Forgetfulness and memory loss

As dementia progresses, brain cells deteriorate making it more and more difficult for the person to make sense of the world and retain information.

Ask yourself:

Would memory prompts help? There are lots of practical ways to cope with increasing forgetfulness. For example, putting notes around the house with the answer to simple questions they might ask, or making sure a calendar and clock remain close by so the person with dementia knows the day and time without having to keep asking.

2. Insecurity

Is the person you're caring for feeling worried or anxious? If the world they live in feels strange and unfamiliar, repeating the same words or behaviour might be a way they've found to comfort themselves.

Ask yourself

Can you say or do something to ease their anxiety? Simply holding their hand, smiling and saying something like 'I'm here for you,' in a soothing voice, might help considerably.

Tip: Don't say, 'You've just asked me that/already said that!' as it will only make them feel more anxious and humiliated.

3. Boredom

If daily life lacks stimulation your loved one might be trying to find a way to provide meaning and purpose.

Ask yourself

If folding the same towel 50 times gives them a sense of purpose, and makes them feel helpful, do you really have to stop them? If possible, you could try to turn the behaviour into a more meaningful activity. For example, if they keep rubbing their hands on a table, give them a cloth or duster.

Tip: Distraction techniques can be very useful if the behaviour is causing you too much stress. For example, try playing a favourite piece of music, get out the photo albums, do craft activities together or do some life story work.

Golden rule:

Generally speaking, it's usually best to look beyond the behaviour itself to work out why it's happening. Try noting down when repetitive behaviour seems to start and look for patterns. For example, do any particular events, activities or emotions make it worse? Does it happen at a particular time of day, or day of the week? The more you understand the reason behind the repetition, the easier it will be for you to cope with it. And with any luck, you might also be able to lessen the need for it too!

4. Relationship Changes

Being a carer is bound to have some impact on your relationship, and on those around you.

Could this be you?

You know you're the right person to be caring for your partner or parent BUT —

- You worry it might permanently damage your relationship.
- You feel uncomfortable doing tasks they used to do.
- You find yourself grieving for the relationship you used to have.

It's hard enough being a carer without having to cope with the emotional rollercoaster that dementia brings with it. But you aren't alone. The vast majority of carers experience a raft of complex feelings and emotions about their changing relationship with the person who has dementia.

Three questions you might ask yourself

1. What's my role?

Your loved one may have been quite happy to take care of the bills and do most of the driving, shopping or cooking. Now you have to do more and more of those things yourself — it's not a role that fits naturally, in fact it's often a struggle.

Tip: Ask for help. Taking over finances or home maintenance can be daunting so enlist the help of other family members or friends. The more adept you become at handling the practical changes, the more confident you will feel about dealing with the emotional ones.

2. Where are my friends?

Despite growing awareness, dementia still carries a stigma which can result in friends or family you used to rely on or enjoy spending time with, avoiding you because they don't know how to handle it. This, in turn, could lead you and the person you're caring for to feel lonely and isolated or struggle with depression.

Tip: Make contact with the people who've drifted away. Encourage them to visit or ask them to help in a different way. For example, maybe they could drive you to a hospital appointment or help you work out what's wrong with the boiler?

3. What's happened to my family?

You might have been a close, loving family and assumed you'd all support each other after the dementia diagnosis. Instead you've been squabbling and rowing about what to do, and can't find any common ground on the financial or legal issues such as Power of Attorney.

Tip: Keep talking. Once you've all had time to get used to the diagnosis (it might take some people longer than others so try be patient), call a family meeting and find some common ground. If you still disagree take professional advice or get help from online communities. Try not to fall out. Remember, your loved one needs as much support, from as many people as possible — and so do you.

How to cope with...

1. Anger

Why?

Being diagnosed with dementia can make many people feel angry at the sheer injustice of it. Unfortunately it's often those closest to them (both physically and emotionally) who bear the brunt. A partner or parent who was once calm and quiet may now be prone to angry outbursts and aggression which seem to be mainly directed at you.

What might help?

Take time out. It's important for both of you to have some space away from each other. Carers all need regular 'me time' and people with dementia need social stimulation. Maybe they could go to a day centre, visit a friend, or take up a new hobby that gets them out of the house. You may also want to look into setting up some respite care.

2. Loss

Why?

You used to be honest and vulnerable with each other, share common interests and talk about things that mattered. Now you can't help feeling sad about all you seem to have lost.

What might help?

Find common ground. Try to focus on activities and tasks you both still enjoy and can still share. For example, you may not be able to do the crossword together anymore, but you could go for walks, cook together, listen to music together or watch a favourite film. Simply enjoying each other's company could make you feel closer and more positive.

3. Changes in your sex life

Why?

Dementia can often mean big changes to intimate relationships. Differing sex drives and changing roles can make sexual intimacy an area of great uncertainty and worry for both of you.

What might help?

Stay positive. Dementia doesn't have to mean the end of a happy sex life. Many couples find new ways to enjoy physical intimacy and closeness by keeping an open mind about what 'sex' means to them, and then working out ways to achieve it. You could also talk to other carers in our community to find out how they've managed this very personal issue.

 Good to know

Dementia can also bring some welcome changes. For example, the person who used to be very quiet and reserved could become more outgoing and willing to have fun with the grandchildren. The person who used to spend hours cleaning the house might now prefer to dance or sing, and the person who found it difficult to say 'I love you' may have no such trouble now. So be ready to embrace these changes and enjoy them as much as you can!

COOL IT!
How to keep your temper in the most difficult of circumstances

If you've always considered yourself a kind, caring person it can come as quite a shock to find yourself becoming snappy, irritable and angry with a loved one who has dementia. But even the calmest carer can lose it occasionally.

Here are a few scenarios that might seem familiar — and some ways to fi them.

Flashpoint 1: Why are you yelling at me?

Dealing with anger and aggression from the person you're caring for can be so upsetting that it's no wonder you can find yourself shouting back, or getting involved in a ridiculous argument about what day it is or whether or not they've had their lunch.

Fix it

Take a step back and try to see aggressive behaviour for what it is; a common symptom of a common illness. Try giving yourself a mantra, such as, 'this isn't personal and many carers like me struggle to cope with it.'

Get out and about (see Chapter Five for ideas) as a change of scenery could be just what you both need.

Flashpoint 2: Stop asking me that!

Repetitive behaviour can drive you potty. Sometimes you can answer the question 'what am I doing today?' countless times without flinching, but at other times your patience quickly wears thin.

Fix it

Phone a friend. Many carers feel they 'should' manage on their own but the reality is that a bit of sympathy and support can go a long way to make a bad day feel better. You could also do whatever you can to keep the person informed. If they keep asking what day it is every five minutes, put a large dementia-friendly calendar day planner or menu board on the wall right in front of them so they have the information they need and don't need to ask you.

Flashpoint 3: Did you do that deliberately?

You have planned a much-needed night out, but just as you're about to leave the person you're caring for has 'an accident' and now you're going to be late. Sometimes you wonder if they do it on purpose because they don't like you going out...

Fix it

It's highly unlikely that this behaviour is deliberate but it could be a sign of anxiety. Does your loved one worry when you go out? What could you do to help ease their anxiety? Or maybe it's your anxiety their sensing? Do you find yourself fretting before going out? Could you manage your own stress better?

There are lots of strategies to help you deal with incontinence so don't let this become an excuse for you to stop going out.

Flashpoint 4: I'm too tired to deal with this

You rarely get a full night's sleep anymore and by early evening you're ready to collapse on the sofa. Unfortunately, this also happens to be the time of day when your loved one's behaviour deteriorates. Coping with exhaustion would test anyone's patience so it's no wonder you flip.

Fix it

Learn a few relaxation techniques, put on some favourite, calming music or a feel-good movie and focus on helping you both to calm down — rather than on the household chores that need to be done. Living well with dementia means enjoying each moment — everything else can wait!

What if you still lose it?

Don't beat yourself up for being human. Instead:

1. Give up on guilt.

Unless you're a saint, losing your temper is unfortunate but inevitable so learn from it and move on.

2. Work out your triggers.

Was it one of the flashpoints above — or something different? Knowing how to recognise your triggers could really help you avoid them in the future.

3. What are you really angry about?

Once they've calmed down, most carers admit that it isn't their loved one they're angry with... it's the situation they find themselves in, and feelings of helplessness and fear which often occur during the dementia journey. You may find yourself feeling angrier at particular times of year; birthdays, wedding anniversaries or Christmas, for example.

4. Practice acceptance.

Learning to accept what you can't change might feel difficult, but it could make life seem much more bearable. If you need help with this, consider Cognitive Behavioural Therapy (CBT). Ask your GP for a referral to a CBT therapist. You should be able to get at least six free sessions on the NHS and many people find it helpful.

Four more quick fixes

- Walk away — sounds obvious perhaps, but have you tried it?
- Punch a pillow — or scream in the car (on your own).
- Go for a run or brisk walk — physical activity can be a great way to release frustration and boost your mood.
- Write it down — keeping a journal is therapeutic and can be a great way to work out flashpoints and triggers.

Chapter 3: Every day dilemmas

As the dementia journey progresses, many carers find they are regularly faced with complex ethical and moral dilemmas, as they try to balance 'doing what's right' with 'doing what's best' for their loved one. Here are a few ways to cope with these difficult every day issues.

Telling Lies

Is it acceptable to lie to a person with dementia because you don't want to hurt them by telling the truth? Find out the arguments for and against the use of therapeutic lying.

Could this be you?

You want the person you're caring for to be as happy and content as possible and you hate the idea of lying to them, but

- It might be less upsetting for them than telling the truth.
- How else can you get them to go to the doctor/take a bath/have a shave?

Deciding what to do is a personal decision. Here are the pros and cons so you can make up your own mind.

Two reasons to tell a therapeutic lie

It's kinder

This is particularly true when you're faced with awkward questions (such as the ones below), especially ones about people who've passed away. Being told the truth, i.e. 'your husband/wife/sister died ten years ago,' could cause unnecessary anguish and pain. And if you need to do this a lot (because they often forget the same person is dead) imagine how distressing it could become.

It's easier

A white lie which encourages the person you're caring for to take their medication, or eat their breakfast could make a tough day just a little more manageable for you.

 Did you know?

Almost 98 per cent of nurses and care staff admit they have told a white lie to a patient if they believed it to be in their best interests.

Two reasons NOT to lie

It's demeaning

People with dementia deserve to be treated with respect and some people still believe that lying to them — even if you do think it's 'for their own good' — can't be justified.

You might get found out

Dementia is a complex illness so there's no guarantees that the person you 'lied to' won't remember the fact you told them their mum/sister/husband would be coming to see them 'at tea time' but didn't turn up. This, in turn, could cause them to lose trust in you.

 **Good to know**

You don't always have to tell an outright lie. Instead you could simply try:

Saying nothing

If your mum thinks she works in the day centre you visit every week, do you really need to tell her the truth and correct her mistake? Is there any harm in saying nothing and playing along, especially if it brings her a sense of purpose and satisfaction?

Bending the truth

If your husband keeps asking 'where's my dad? Some carers side-step the question by saying something like, 'don't worry, he's safe' instead of saying he died 30 years ago. Or you could try changing the subject slightly by asking 'where would he normally be at this time?'

Tip: Is it in their best interests? If you're unsure what to do, remember that the best Person Centred Care focuses on the uniqueness of each person and each dementia journey. So if you feel a therapeutic lie is in the best interests of the person you love, perhaps you need to trust your instinct.

Feel guilty?

If you do find it necessary to lie to a loved one, try not to feel bad about it. Instead, see the bigger truth; the person you're caring for deserves to feel calm, safe and respected. Constantly correcting them, by bringing them back to reality, may not only cause sadness and pain, it could also destroy their dignity and peace.

Awkward Questions

At some point your loved one with dementia will ask you something that you find tricky to answer, mainly because you don't want to cause them any unnecessary suffering.

Here's some of the most common sorts of questions you might be faced with.

1. Questions about loved ones who are dead

They say: **'Where is my mum/dad/husband/best friend?'**

Why?

As the illness progresses and their recent memory disappears, events from the distant past can become very vivid for people with dementia. So if they ask after a loved one who died decades ago, it could simply mean that they've been thinking about them recently or that something has triggered a memory of them which they'd like to share.

You say: **'Oh, I was just thinking about them myself. Remember that day we....'**

Why?

You aren't ignoring the question, just side-stepping it and leading the conversation into a more pleasant area for both of you.

Or

You say: **'I'm sure they'd love to see you but they can't get here. Tell me more about them, what would they say if they were here with you?'**

Why?

This is a satisfying answer which isn't, strictly speaking, a lie but does involve being fairly economical with the truth.

You say: **'They can't see you because they're at work/shopping/at school.'**

Why?

Now you definitely are lying, but many people (experts and carers) believe this sort of therapeutic lying is acceptable and sometimes necessary if it's in the best interests of the person with dementia.

2. Questions about where they live now

They say: **'When are we going home? I want to go home now! Can you call me a taxi?'**

Why?

People with dementia can become very anxious and afraid if their environment suddenly feels unfamiliar. If they've recently moved house — whether into a care home or in with family — this sort of question can crop up frequently.

You say: **'Who will be at home now?'**

Why?

'Home' could mean lots of things for people with dementia. It could be their childhood home, or their home when they were newly married. This sort of question allows you to explore what time
period they're talking about. Once you know, you can steer the conversation towards general chat about the era.

Tip: Look beyond what they're saying. If they suddenly seem to hate where they're living now it doesn't necessarily mean you made the wrong choice, so try not to take it personally. Instead, consider what feelings may have led them to say this and how you can help them cope with the feeling. For example, could you put on some favourite music or look through a favourite photo album to remind them of familiar places and people.

3. Questions about their illness

They say: **'What's wrong with me? Am I going mad?'**

Why?

Many people with dementia have moments of clarity and lucidity when they suddenly seem to understand exactly what's happening — and are, understandably, terrified.

You say: **'You certainly are not going mad!'**

Why?

You are telling the truth and providing absolute reassurance which should help to ease their fear. Whether you choose to elaborate your answer further — for example, by saying, 'You've got memory problems', or just telling them they have vascular dementia or Alzheimer's, depends on how much you think they need to know in order to feel calmer.

Still struggling?

Try not to worry. There are no right or wrong answers to any awkward questions and, sadly, no perfect solutions either. Balancing the need for respect and truth with kindness and compassion is a daily, sometimes hourly, struggle for anyone who cares for a person with dementia. Remember, you aren't alone.

Taking Risks

You want to keep your loved one with dementia safe, but you also want them to enjoy life as much as possible. So how do you get the balance right?

Could this be you?

You know you can't wrap them in cotton wool and that the person you're caring for needs to make the most of each and every day, BUT —

- They're vulnerable and you need to protect them.
- It would be irresponsible to let them do certain things.
- You'd never forgive yourself if they came to any harm.

The vast majority of carers have the same understandable concerns, but it is possible to find a way to overcome your worries so that your loved one can continue to enjoy life to the full.

Why take risks?

Life is full of risks — there really is no escaping them. It's not only impossible to keep the person you love away from risks, it might not be in their best interests either. Staying at home all day with you might be the 'safest' option, but it probably won't be the most enjoyable, and it could make life very boring. This, in turn, may leave them feeling lonely and isolated or frustrated and prone to angry outbursts. Besides, Person Centred Care means respecting the rights and opinions of the person with dementia, even if some of the activities or tasks they want to do involve risk-taking.

Ask yourself

Did they take risks before having dementia? For example, did they enjoy sailing, skiing or taking part in any other activities with clear risks involved? Some people are bigger risk takers than others and understanding the sort of risk-taker your loved one has always been is a good indication of how they would like to live now.

Still not convinced?

Don't worry, you're bound to feel a bit uncomfortable. After all, this approach might challenge some of your most basic assumptions about your role as a carer.

Try to change your mind

When we think about taking risks, most of us associate them with danger, fear and uncertainty. However, risk-taking can also have many positive outcomes. For example, if the risk pays off, a person with dementia might gain a huge confidence boost, and a sense of satisfaction which far outweighs the initial risk.

So instead of this:

Risk = Danger

Think this:

Risk = Reward

Risk v Danger — what's the difference?

Risk taking in ordinary life is normal and necessary for everyone, including people with dementia who retain their rights to choice and control, and this will inevitably bring an element of risk.

Risks can't be eliminated...but negligence can. There's a big difference between taking a measured, calculated risk which has been carefully discussed with everyone involved, and making a rash decision without thinking it through or fully understanding the consequences.

The balancing act

Whether it's allowing someone with dementia to catch a bus into town, prepare their own meal, or fly to Australia to visit loved ones, the steps you need to take when assessing the risks involved, are broadly the same.

1.   Identify and list possible hazards and dangers

For example, they might catch the wrong bus, or get lost in town. They might burn themselves on an oven, or take ill on a long-haul flight.

2. Ask yourself: How likely is it they'll come to harm?

For example, could you take them to the bus stop yourself, make sure they have an identity card with them and a simple mobile phone. Could you consider using a tracking device? Could you make the kitchen as dementia-friendly as possible to limit the risk of accidents, or turn the cooker off and leave a selection of cold meats, salads, bread and cheese for them to create their own cold lunch?

3. What might be the severity of the harm?

If a long haul flight really could make them terribly ill, it might not be worth taking (you probably wouldn't be able to get travel insurance anyway) but if the worst thing that could happen when they're in town on their own is that you have to go and collect them because they got lost — maybe that's a risk worth taking? If making their own lunch gives them a sense of control, achievement and normality, surely that too has to be worth considering?

4. Identify and list positive benefits

Make this as detailed as possible, outlining the physical, emotional and social benefits of taking this particular risk. For example, a trip to town provides physical activity, getting there on their own will be a great confidence boost, and meeting other people will provide social stimulation.

Two ways to reduce risks

1. Make use of technology

Everything from GPS tracking devices to a simple mobile phone can enable someone with dementia to take risks which will allow them to maintain a sense of independence and control in their own lives.

2. Share stories

Talking to other carers, families and friends of those living with dementia can be a great way to get support, tips and motivation to do something different.

 Good to know

As awareness of dementia continues to grow, dementia friendly communities are beginning to emerge which should lessen the risks of people with dementia having a bad experience when they're out on their own.

A law you should know about

The Mental Capacity Act 2005 is designed to protect and empower vulnerable people who are unable to make important decisions for themselves. These are the essential facts worth knowing.

In a nutshell

Being free to make your own decisions (even if they're ones that other people don't approve of) is a fundamental human right and one which the law takes very seriously. The Mental Capacity Act might have a grim sounding name but it was put in place for good reasons.

It has two basic functions:

1. It tells people what to do and how they can do it if someone can't make decisions on their own.

2. It spells out very carefully what the term 'lacking capacity' actually means so that it cannot be open to abuse.

What does the law say?

There are five key principles to the Mental Capacity Act 2005,

- Every adult has the right to make their own decisions if they have the capacity to do so. Family carers and healthcare or social care staff must assume that a person has the capacity to make decisions, unless it can be established that they don't.

- People should receive support, and all possible steps should be taken, to help them make their own decisions.

- People have the right to make decisions that others might think are unwise, and this should not automatically result in them being labelled as 'lacking capacity'.
- Any act done for, or any decision made on behalf of, someone who lacks capacity must be in their best interests.
- Any act done for, or any decision made on behalf of, someone who lacks capacity should be an option that is less restrictive of their basic rights and freedoms — as long as it is still in their best interests.

Do they lack capacity?

If the person you love cannot do any or all of the following it may be that they do, in the legal sense, 'lack capacity'.

- Understand information given to them.
- Retain information long enough to be able to make a decision.
- Weigh up the information available to make a decision.
- Communicate their decision.

Are you acting in their 'best interests?'

If you're caring for someone with dementia it's really important to be aware of what this term actually means:

- The person who lacks capacity must be involved in decisions as much as possible.
- You must be aware of their wishes and feelings.
- You must also consult with other people involved in their care.
- You should not make any assumptions based on their age, appearance, condition or behaviour.
- You need to consider whether the person you're acting for is likely to regain capacity to make the decision in the future.

So: If you've tried your best to comply with all the points above, then it's probably safe to say you are legally acting in your loved one's best interests.

SPECAL Care: Could It Help You?

Find out about a unique approach to dementia care which, although sometimes considered controversial, might be able to help you cope with some of the dilemmas in this chapter.

What is SPECAL dementia care?

The main aim of Specialised Early Care for Alzheimer's (known as SPECAL) is to keep someone with dementia feeling calm and contended, even if it means that the carer becomes reliant on therapeutic lying and reminiscence therapy as ways to ensure this happens.

Some carers swear by the SPECAL approach, saying it's made their loved ones feel happier and more confident, lessened challenging behaviour such as anger and aggression, and has even reduced their need for medication.

However others say the SPECAL approach is demeaning to those with dementia, difficult to implement and far too simplistic.

Here's what you need to know so you can make up your own mind.

Three golden rules

The SPECAL approach advises carers to stick to these rules:

1. Don't ask direct questions

This includes anything from, 'what would you like to wear today?' to 'what shall I cook for lunch?' Direct questions are simply too stressful for someone with dementia who may not have enough factual reserves or cognitive ability to answer them. Realising they don't 'know' the answer can then make them feel upset and anxious.

Giving a simple choice, such as, 'would you like to wear your red skirt or the blue trousers' (hold them up so they can see them, too). Or, 'Do you fancy chicken or fish for lunch?' These are far easier questions to answer but should still ensure your loved one has choice and feels respected.

2. Listen and learn from the person with dementia

Feelings are more important than facts in SPECAL care which places far more emphasis on making the person with dementia feel good even if this means telling therapeutic lies or half-truths in response to awkward questions, particularly questions concerning loved ones who've passed away.

Instead try

Saying, 'your mum can't visit today'. It's far kinder than, 'your mum died 20 years ago.'

3. Don't contradict

If your loved one insists that it's 1964, try to stop yourself from correcting them. The past may feel far more real to them than the present. After all, memories from 1964 are probably easier to recall than those from yesterday. If they want to 'live' in 1964 right now, and it makes them feel happy, why should you try to stop them?

 Did you know?

The SPECAL method was developed by Penny Garner whilst caring for her mum Dorothy who had Alzheimer's. When Penny's son-in-law, the psychologist Oliver James, heard about it, he wrote the best-selling book Contented Dementia in 2009 which explained the approach in detail.

For

Those in favour of SPECAL care say:

- It places the wellbeing of the person with dementia at the heart of the care — so it is entirely person-centred.
- It works positively with dementia, rather than trying to ignore or defeat it.
- It can bring a massive improvement in the quality of life of those living with dementia and their families.

Against

Those who have doubts about SPECAL care say:

- It takes away choice and control from people with dementia.
- It encourages 'systematic' deception.
- It claims to work for 'everyone' with dementia, but every person — and every dementia journey — is unique.

In conclusion

Many carers who come across SPECAL find some of its recommendations very helpful, others realise they were already 'doing some of it' anyway and feel reassured. Generally speaking, most people gain something positive from knowing about the SPECAL approach.

Chapter 4: Why Does It Happen?

One of the hardest parts of the dementia journey is learning how to cope with difficult behaviour from a person you love, trust and have probably known for years. Here's why it might happen and what you can do to manage it.

Personality Changes

It can be very upsetting to watch a loved one behave in a way that's out of character. Find out how to cope when dementia causes disturbing behaviour changes.

Could this be you?

You're able to cope with most of the challenges of caring for a loved one with dementia but it can sometimes seem as if they've undergone a personality transplant. Character traits you used to know and love such as empathy, patience or wittiness have almost disappeared. Instead, they shout, swear and embarrass you in public — what's going on?

Don't panic

As distressing as it may be to watch and experience, out of character behaviour can be a fairly common symptom of dementia. The illness doesn't only affect memory, it can also affect parts of the brain that control personality and inhibitions, particularly frontotemporal dementia, which can involve substantial changes in personality.

 Did you know?

Frontotemporal dementia damages the frontal lobes of the brain which are responsible for personality and social inhibitions. If the person you're caring for is living with frontotemporal dementia it might profoundly alter their character and the way they behave in public. For example, they may undress, make sexual advances, or even steal.

Six common behaviour changes

1. Rage

They yell, scream, swear, pick fights — even physical ones — and are prone to full blown temper tantrums.

2. Loss of inhibition

They make rude comments to strangers, family or carers. For example, 'Look how fat she is!' Or 'I've never really liked you.' They might also touch their private parts in public or try to take off their clothes.

3. Hiding and hoarding

They refuse to throw anything away, even if it's falling apart. They've bought so much food/washing powder/loo roll that there's nowhere left to store it. You sometimes find it stuffed behind cupboards or under beds, but they still keep going out and buying more.

4. Paranoia

They obsessively count money or examine bank statements then accuse carers/children/friends of stealing or spying on them. A partner might be accused of having an affair, or of selling their favourite possessions.

5. Neglecting personal hygiene

They refuse to take a bath or shower, hate brushing their teeth, rarely wash their hair and would wear the same clothes every day if you didn't take them away and wash them.

6. Passivity

A once gregarious, sociable person now sits in a chair all day, reluctant to do anything, go anywhere or even say very much.

Six ways to deal with it:

1. Look for meaning behind the behaviour

However out of character the behaviour, there is often a reason for it — and it's sometimes more obvious than you might imagine. For example, could trying to take their clothes off mean they're feeling too hot? Could refusing to bathe be because they've forgotten how to, or are afraid to be in the bathroom?

2. Learn the value of distraction

If their behaviour is embarrassing, try to distract, play it down, or ignore it whenever possible. For example, if they make an embarrassing comment, try changing the subject very quickly to something more pleasant. For example, if they're criticising other people's appearance try a compliment, 'you're looking very smart yourself today. I love what you're wearing. Shall we do some window shopping now, or do you fancy a cup of tea?'

3. Be alert to early warning signs

Notice when trouble might be brewing and you'll have a better chance of limiting it or reducing its impact. For example, if they didn't sleep very well they might be more likely to become angry or aggressive. Try playing some soothing music or suggest a nap and talk in a gentle voice. Could passivity be a sign they're feeling depressed or lonely?

4. Try not to take it personally

This might not be easy, but if you can keep reminding yourself that their behaviour is a symptom of dementia — it's their illness talking, not them — it can make even the most outrageous behaviour easier to bear.

5. Step into their shoes

It might help give you a new perspective. For example, perhaps hoarding is a sign they're afraid. Obsessively holding on to possessions might be the only way they have to retain precious memories of the past. Could you try to be more patient, or even light-hearted about it? Humour can be a great way to ease tension and create a calmer atmosphere which could, in turn, make their behaviour easier to manage. Putting together a memory book or memory box with some choice items that really stir happy memories might be a nice way for them to maintain them without having to hoard items away.

6. Take a break

Never underestimate what a difficult job you are doing and the importance of having regular 'me-time' and respite care (see Chapter Seven). A change of scenery could be one of the best ways to relax and recharge your batteries.

Anger and Aggression

Dealing with aggressive behaviour can be really tricky. However, once you begin to understand the reason behind the behaviour (which is often totally out of character) you can start to make sense of it and learn to respond in a way that helps limit it.

Aggressive behaviour can be either verbal, such as swearing, screaming and shouting, or physical, such as hitting, pinching, scratching, hair-pulling and biting.

BUT — it's important to remember that aggression isn't a universal symptom of dementia — some people will get it, and some won't.

Causes of aggression

1. Physical discomfort
2. The environment
3. Social issues
4. Psychological problems

1. Physical discomfort

If the person you're caring for is ill or in pain, they may lash out because the pain makes them feel confused or frightened — they simply don't understand it.

It could be down to illnesses such as a bladder or throat infection, or they may feel uncomfortable because they're constipated or thirsty. And don't forget about any long-term health issues which could be causing discomfort, such as arthritis, or the affect that medications could be having on their mental wellbeing.

2. The environment

Is the room too bright, noisy, crowded, hot, cold or just generally over-simulating? This could make someone with dementia feel lost or overwhelmed and then lash out in fear or frustration.

3. Social issues

Find out if the person you're caring for is lonely, bored or lacking social contact. They may need some sensory stimulation.

If other people are involved in their care, it's worth finding out if there have been any changes recently. For example, if a favourite carer is on holiday it might make someone with dementia feel unsafe, and start acting aggressively.

4. Psychological problems

Dementia affects your perception and understanding of the outside world. If you feel as if your rights are being ignored – as some people do – it can make you want to lash out.

Changes in the brain can also make people living with dementia feel more extreme reactions than they used to. So whereas before they might have reacted with frustration if they felt someone was being rude to them, now they respond with violence.

Dementia can also cause hallucinations, delusions and paranoia, which can lead to aggression, as they don't really understand what is going on. If the person you're caring for doesn't recognise where they are, or who you are, they might think you're a stranger trying to hurt them. So it makes sense that they might lash out and hit you – wouldn't you do the same?

How should you respond to aggressive behaviour?

Being on the receiving end of aggressive behaviour caused by dementia is undoubtedly difficult and often traumatic. However there are steps you can take to manage it both now and in the future.

There's no 'one size fits all' answer, but generally speaking it's best to:

- Try to stay calm
- Identify the cause
- Step into their shoes
- Reassure and listen
- Use distraction tactics
- Don't punish them
- Talk to a friend

1. Try to stay calm

While this might seem easier said than done, an angry or defensive response could make the situation worse. Try not to show any fear or alarm, take a deep breath and step back to give them some space to calm down.

2. Identify the cause

This won't always be obvious, but think about what happened immediately before they became violent and ask yourself if that could have triggered it. For example, could they be in pain or uncomfortable, and can you remedy it?

3. Step into their shoes

Try to look at the situation from their perspective. If they've reacted strongly after you've tried to bathe them or helped them use the toilet, it could be because they feel embarrassed or ashamed. Even though you know you're only trying to help, dementia can mean the person you're caring for no longer has the same level of reasoning or logic.

4. Reassure and listen

Once they have stopped acting violently, and are willing for you to approach them, maintain eye contact and talk in a low, soothing (but not patronising) voice. Explain calmly that you want to help and listen if they're able to tell you what the problem is.

5. Use distraction tactics

Try shifting the focus to another activity if you think this is what is causing the aggression, or pick a pastime that is more relaxing, such as listening to music or going for a walk with them.

6. Don't punish them

It can be easy to feel like you want to scold the person like a naughty toddler when they've been aggressive, but they probably have no real concept of what they've done wrong, or why it's inappropriate (and may not even remember the incident the next day).

7. Talk to a friend

Try to avoid unleashing your frustrations on the person you're caring for. Make time to meet with friends who understand your situation, talk to your GP, a counsellor or a dementia support worker, or even vent your feelings on a blog or forum. There will be other people out there who are in the same boat.

What about next time?

If you're worried this could be the first of many aggressive incidents, think about how you might be able to prevent it happening in the future.

Make a note of the incident so you'll remember exactly how it panned and what potential 'triggers' you can avoid. For example, if it was caused when you tried to help with bathing and washing, find out what products are available to help them maintain some independence in this area and reduce the risk of further flare-ups.

Look for common signs that they might be in pain. For example, rubbing or pulling at an area of the body, a change in appetite, a temperature or swelling and inflammation.

Expect some trial and error when working out how to manage aggressive behaviour, particularly as the person your caring for may not react in the same way the next time. However, the more 'triggers' you are able to pin down and learn how to avoid, the more likely it is that you can curb distressing outbursts in the future.

 **Good to know**

In the past, people who developed aggressive tendencies related to dementia were prescribed anti-psychotic drugs. There's now a strong move away from the use of these drugs, and if they are used, it should only be as the very last resort and for a minimal amount of time.

Sundowning

If behaviour difficulties only seem to happen later in the day, the person you're caring for could be experiencing a condition called sundowning. Here's what you need to know...

Could this be you?

Your loved one generally seems calm and content for most of the day but from around 4pm onwards they change and:

• Become agitated, irritated and aggressive

• Start yelling or pacing up and down

• Are unable to settle or sleep until very late at night

Sundowning is not a disease but a collection of symptoms which tend to occur at the end of the day and into the night, and might become increasingly common as their dementia progresses.

 Did you know?

As many as 1 in 5 people with dementia may develop sundowning though it can also happen to older people without dementia.

Your checklist: Five questions to ask yourself

1. Are they physically or mentally exhausted?

After a busy day, people with dementia can find it very difficult to unwind, making them more likely to become agitated, angry and unreasonable. So one of the best things you can do for them is to help them relax.

Tip: Consider relaxation techniques put on some soothing music or a meditation/sounds of nature CD, turn off a loud TV or radio and dim very bright lights (but not too much — dark shadows on walls can appear frightening to someone with dementia who might also have visual diffi ulties).

Most research reveals that sundowning is most likely to happen in the middle stages of dementia and continue for a few months or into the later stages.

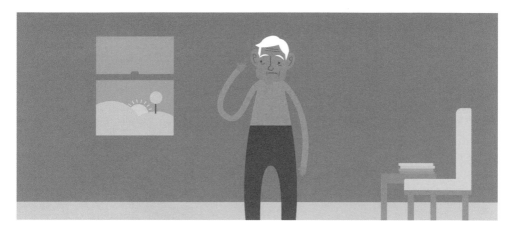

Does any particular event seem to trigger sundowning?

Does the change in their behaviour coincide with a family member coming home from work or school, or with loud music going on, or a vacuum cleaner being used?

Tip: Could they sit in the garden, or a quieter room while this is happening? Or perhaps they could put on headphones and continue listening to a CD?

Are they napping during the day?

If sleep seems to escape them until the early hours it could be that they're having too much of it during the day. Hours of sleeping can confuse the body's circadian rhythms and keep older people wide awake at night. Or perhaps they aren't getting enough physical activity and need to get outside more during the day.

Tip: Take another look at their daily care plan. Could you schedule in a walk outside, an exercise DVD or some light gardening? Any activity which provides stimulation should help them to stop nodding off.

Do they seem lost in thought?

It's natural for older people to sometimes contemplate the past, to reflect on how life has changed, and remember the people they've loved and lost, but if your loved one seems to be dwelling too much on sad thoughts and becoming preoccupied with them later in the day or evening, it won't only increase feelings of loneliness and isolation, it could also lead to upsetting behaviour and restlessness.

Tip: Give them something meaningful to do which will focus their mind, but without being too taxing. Hobbies, including crafts and games, can be particularly useful. For example, painting, making jewellery, or colouring in. Or perhaps they could fold the laundry for you (they can do it sitting down), watch a favourite feel-good movie together, or talk to friends or relatives on the phone? Activities which make them feel connected to the world should help to boost their mood and make the evening more enjoyable for both of you.

Are YOU physically or mentally exhausted?

After a busy day you're probably desperate for a sit down. Finding yourself on the receiving end of an angry outburst or having to deal with some very difficult behaviour, is the last thing you want or need. BUT — if you show your frustration there's a chance you could make sundowning behaviour even worse.

Tip: Ask for help. Caring for someone with dementia is incredibly hard, and caregiver stress and depression is all too common. If you need the support of a friend or relative, then say so.

Hallucinations

If your loved one has already experienced a hallucination you may have found it very scary and difficult to watch. Find out what you need to know about them and the best way to cope.

In a nutshell

A hallucination can involve seeing, hearing, smelling, feeling, tasting (or a combination of them all) something that isn't there. Hallucinations are caused by changes in the brain which, if they occur at all, usually happen in the middle or later stages of the dementia journey. Hallucinations are more common in dementia with Lewy bodies and Parkinson's dementia, but they can also occur in Alzheimer's and other types of dementia.

BUT

- There's a difference between a hallucination and a delusion, which is usually caused by paranoia or suspicious feelings and thoughts.
- Some 'hallucinations' are simply visual mistakes caused by eye sight problems which are quite common in people with dementia (see below).

 Did you know?

Around one in 10 people with dementia with Lewy bodies experience olfactory hallucinations — smells that aren't really there.

Is it really a hallucination?

First make sure that what you're dealing with is a hallucination caused by dementia and not simply the result of:

Eye sight problems

Dementia can affect sight and vision in many different ways. For example, a person with dementia might mistake a reflection in the mirror for an intruder or think people on TV are in the room with them. They could also have problems recognising familiar faces or become wary of familiar environments, for example, a shiny floor might look wet, a shadow in a corner might look like a hole.

So before assuming they're having an hallucination, arrange a sight test with an optician and make sure each room in the home is well lit and dementia-friendly.

Other health issues

A kidney or bladder infection, alcohol, and certain medications (such as some anti-depressants, stroke or migraine medication and drugs for Parkinson's) can also cause confusion and lead to hallucinations.

Dealing with hallucinations

- Don't try to reason with your loved one because it simply won't work. In fact, knowing you don't believe them might make them even more upset and agitated

- Do stay calm. Your loved one isn't going mad, what they're seeing is simply a symptom of their illness. You could try saying something such as 'Don't worry, I'll take care of you, I'm here to protect you.'

- Don't pretend you can see or hear what they can. It won't help and it could make your loved one even more confused or agitated.

- Do check your environment. Turn off the TV, turn on lights so the room is well lit, and turn off anything that might be triggering a hallucination such as a TV, a computer, a radio.

- Don't diminish their experience. Saying 'Oh, don't be silly there's nothing there', is quite demeaning because it belittles what they're seeing, which to them is very real.

- Do be kind and acknowledge how your loved one might be feeling during the hallucination. For example, 'It sounds very scary, I can see how upset you are.'

- Do distract the person you're caring for if possible. For example, if they're hearing voices that aren't there, try chatting to them. It's harder to hear voices if someone is really talking to you. If they can 'see' someone, sit facing them and get eye contact if you can. Again, if they can see you clearly during the hallucination it could make the experience less powerful and less intense.

Need more help?

If your loved one is still becoming very distressed by hallucinations:

1. See your GP but make sure you take some notes with you about the hallucinations. For example, how long they last, what they involve, what time of day they happen and details of any medication they might already be taking.

2. If nothing else seems to help, you may want to consider anti-psychotic medication. Anti-psychotics do carry risks and have, unfortunately, often been oversubscribed in the past, but they can be very effective in reducing or stopping hallucinations, so don't automatically discount them if your loved one is really suffering.

If the person you're caring for has dementia with Lewy Bodies any prescription for anti-psychotics must be strictly monitored and regularly reviewed.

 Good to know

Many carers say that activities which help to reduce anxiety such as <u>art</u> or music therapy, reminiscence or pet therapy, have helped their loved ones cope with hallucinations.

Suspicion and Paranoia

If the person you're caring for is in the grips of a delusion or becoming paranoid and suspicious it can also take every ounce of energy and love to manage.

What is a delusion?

When someone is deluded, it means that they have a distinct set of beliefs, which are false, but which they believe to be true.

Often, the delusion will lead to extreme suspicion, with the person affected thinking that people around them — family, carers, friends — are trying to trick them.

Delusions can take many forms, but often revolve around a number of paranoid scenarios such as believing that someone is trying to steal their possessions, that someone is following them, or that there is a stranger in the house trying to get them.

 Did you know?

It's fairly common. About 40 per cent of people living with dementia experience delusions.

What is paranoia?

Paranoia can occur as a result of delusion. It is centred round suspicions and can become a way for the person with dementia to project feelings of fear. Paranoia can also be caused by hallucinations.

What causes delusions and paranoia?

When someone has dementia, glitches within their brains cause memory problems and changes in personality. If there's a hole in their memory, they may try to fill in that faulty memory with a delusion that makes sense to them. Their confusion and inability to remember objects or recognise faces contributes to the development of untrue beliefs.

So, if they've forgotten where they left their wallet, and a new carer has just started visiting them, they may simply assume that this new person has stolen the wallet. If you're caring for a loved one he might accuse you of being unfaithful or trying to poison them, all of which is extremely traumatic.

However, there are some simple steps which can help, no matter how difficult the situation may seem.

Don't take it personally

If they suddenly start accusing you of something, try not to take offence. This is the illness talking, not them. So put yourself in their shoes and listen to what might be behind the accusations.

Don't argue or try to convince

Try not to respond with 'Why would I do that?' or 'Don't be silly!' If you attempt to convince the person you're caring for that they're in the wrong, they could end up feeling very agitated and angry that you're not considering their point of view. They'll also feel like you're not listening to them.

Reassure without asking questions

Tell them that you'll help them look for an item if they think it's been moved or stolen. If there's a simple answer, share your thoughts, but don't overwhelm them with clever arguments or a lengthy explanations. If you've been accused of infidelity, don't take it personally. Often fears such as this stem from being abandoned. Once again, provide reassurance and make it clear that you're sticking with them.

Keep a spare set of 'stolen' items

If it always seems to be a specific item that is 'going missing', see if you can have some spare ones ready, such as wallets or spectacles.

Switch focus

If they're still frustrated, suspicious or agitated, try distracting them. For example, say, 'Before we start looking for your book, why don't we have some lunch, then we'll look for it after that?'.

 Good to know

Remember, someone with dementia who is experiencing delusions is simply trying to make sense of their world while dealing with cognitive decline, confusion and fear. Try to ensure that other family members and friends understand this, too, and that they take their lead from you. Remember, you're the expert!

Chapter 5: Getting out and about

Whether it's a short trip to the park or a fortnight's holiday, getting away from home can bring lots of benefits for people with dementia — but where can you go and what can you do without it becoming stressful — or even dangerous? Here's how to make going out a safe, enjoyable experience for both of you.

Could this be you?

You like the idea of getting out and about with the person you're caring for but:

- You can't help worrying — what if they get lost?
- They don't seem bothered about going out
- They can't walk far — where would you go?

You aren't alone. Here's a few ideas to inspire you...

Start small

Fit a small outdoor activity into their daily care plan whenever possible. For example, if you have a garden, make it as safe and interesting as possible and do some gardening together. Or, weather permitting, simply sit outside with a cup of tea.

No garden? No problem

Try the nearest green space or local shop — no more than a ten minute walk away from home. Or find your nearest memory café (see below) for some social support from like-minded people.

Going further

Whether it's a park, a shopping trip, a social group, or a full day out at the sea, follow these three simple rules.

1. Make it safe

Carrying identity cards and a simple mobile phone (see below) and staying close together should ensure you both stay safe. Of course there are no guarantees but if the benefits of going out seem to outweigh the benefits of staying at home, it's surely a risk worth taking — and one they would thank you for.

Tip: If they need to use a public loo don't be afraid to go to the front of the queue and quietly explain. You could also consider showing a simple identity card to anybody who asks. Remember, dementia is a disability and their needs should take priority.

2. Make it fun

Exploring nature can be very enjoyable and a great mood booster for both of you, so whether it's being guided around a park, taking a woodland walk, or having a picnic, just do what they can manage.

Tip: Don't be afraid to go out in bad weather. As long as they're wrapped up warm and wearing suitable clothing, being in the fresh air and feeling the wind on their face can still be a welcome distraction.

3. Make it mean something

Take a trip down memory lane. You could go back to an area they used to live or work, near a place they used to visit when the children were young, or a museum they would enjoy (wartime exhibitions can bring back vivid memories) and which you could amble around at your own pace.

Tip: You could take photos of the day so you can create a photo collage or online album to look through a few days later as a memory aid.

Ready to go? Your 5-Point Checklist

It's worth doing a quick check before you head out the door

1. Are they wearing comfortable, sturdy shoes?
2. Will they be warm enough — or too hot?
3. Have they been to the toilet?
4. Have they got ID? Whether it's a name and your phone number sewn into a coat, an identity card in their pocket or an identity bracelet or necklace, it's wise to make sure they have something on them if you're concerned about wandering.
5. Have you got your phone?

Tip: It might be worth giving your loved one a cheap phone, too. Put it in their pocket, without any lock on, and with an 'in case of emergency' phone number, (i.e., your phone number) so if you do get separated and someone tries to help them, they will be able to contact you.

What if they don't want to go?

Whilst some people with dementia absolutely love going out, others get anxious or show little interest in the idea, and might need persuasion and reassurance. If you want to take them to a favourite park try showing them a photograph and having a conversation about a time you've been there before. A bit of reminiscence can make them feel calmer and more positive about trying something different.

Don't just talk and talk and try to persuade them by wearing them down. If they really don't want to budge, you'll have to accept it. Respect their feelings and try again another time.

Don't worry...

...if the outing is a disaster and you end up coming home feeling tired and demoralized. Maybe you were too ambitious? Or maybe they just weren't in the mood.

Next time

*   Choose a different time of day.
*   Stay nearer home.
*   Ask for help — maybe it was too difficult on your own. Don't be afraid to call for support. Whether it's a neighbour, a grandchild, or an old friend of theirs, you might be surprised at how many people are willing to come along with you. The more, the merrier!

Memory cafés

Memory cafés are popping up all over the UK and they can be a great place to go if you're caring for a person with dementia, if you're worried about someone's memory, or if you just want to meet other people who are affected by dementia. Here's what to expect if you visit a memory café.

Three facts worth knowing

1. Memory cafés are usually held on a regular basis, either once a week, once a fortnight, or once a month. Most are located in places that are easy to access, such as a community centre, a village hall, or a local hotel.

2. Tables are laid out 'café style' and tea, coffee and biscuits are served (you might be asked to make a donation to cover the cost of these).

3. Memory cafés are run by people (including volunteers) who have experience and training in dementia, so you should receive a warm welcome. A community nurse is usually on call, too (often sitting in a private area or side room), if you want to have a chat or get some help or advice.

But this is not the same as visiting your doctor. She won't be able to offer a diagnosis or make a referral. A memory café is not the same as a memory clinic where a formal diagnosis of dementia can be made.

Benefits of going to a memory café

- You can both socialise and chat with other like-minded people, and curb feelings of loneliness and isolation.

- You can both have fun! Most cafés provide stimulating activities for carers and people with dementia which can help prevent boredom and aid relaxation. For example, live music, sing-a-longs, quizzes, painting, memory box work, massage and reflexology.

- You can talk about issues that you might be worried about with people who understand.

 Good to know

You can find your nearest memory café by going to www.memorycafes.org.uk

Worried about the loo? Coping with incontinence when you're away from home

Try not to let worries about incontinence keep you and your loved one from going out and enjoying yourselves. Here's how to ease your fears and cope.

Incontinence is a fairly common symptom of dementia, particularly as the illness progresses. But although it can be very upsetting and provoke strong emotions such as shame, embarrassment and helplessness, there are ways to stop it limiting your life. Here's your 4-step plan:

1. Plan ahead

When you're organising a trip out with a person who has dementia, it's always best to think ahead. Whether you're going to the supermarket or for a day at the sea, work out where the nearest toilets are located and how easy they are to access, especially if mobility is an issue. If you're planning a full day out remember to build in enough time for a few trips to public toilets.

2. Prepare

Incontinence pads and pants are discreet and comfortable and there's lots of choice, from disposable pads to washable pants. If the person you're caring for is likely to have an accident, or simply gets stressed by the idea of having an accident, it's worth using them as a preventative measure. This is particularly the case if you're going somewhere you haven't been before (and don't know where the toilets are) or somewhere that's likely to be busy.

Tip: Don't forget to also pack cleaning wipes, barrier creams, bags to put soiled products in and extra underwear to ensure your loved one feels fresh and comfortable for the rest of the day.

3. Prevent

In an ideal world, it's better for you, and the person you're caring for, if you can reach a toilet in time. However, if their dementia is making it more difficult for them to communicate the need directly, try:

- Watching their body language; pacing up and down, pulling at clothes or fidgeting are all signs that they may need the loo.
- Asking regularly, 'would you like to go to the loo?' Even if they're bladder is strong, they'll probably need to go at least every couple of hours.
- Buying a RADAR key (see below)
- Getting a 'Just can't wait card' from The Bladder and Bowel Foundation, which should allow you to jump queues for public toilets. (These are free but you might be asked to make a £5 donation).

4. Don't Panic

If, despite all your efforts, the person with dementia still has an accident, try not to get irritated with them. Remember, it isn't their fault and providing they were wearing a pad, it shouldn't cause them too much distress, and won't take too long to sort out. Reassure them that it isn't a big deal. Try saying something calming such as, 'Accidents happen and there's no harm done.' Take them to a loo (preferably a disabled toilet so you can both get in comfortably) and help them get cleaned up. Keep reminding them it isn't their fault and not to let it spoil the day out.

- Don't limit fluids — dehydration could make them even more confused.
- Do run them a bubble bath when you get home and encourage them to have a good soak. It will relax them and should also help to get rid of any lingering, unpleasant odours.

 **Good to know**

If the person you care for seems to be having more accidents than they would normally, it's worth investigating other reasons for it, rather than simply assuming their dementia is the cause and there's nothing you can do. For example, Urinary Tract Infections (UTI's) can increase the likelihood and frequency of incontinence.

What are RADAR keys?

As dementia progresses, many people find it increasingly difficult to 'hold on' if they need to use a toilet. Finding a disabled loo — then discovering it's locked — is hugely frustrating, and waiting in a long queue for a public toilet can be stressful....this is where Radar keys come in useful.

Four facts about Radar keys

1. A Radar key gives access to public toilets designed for disabled people. These toilets are often kept locked to prevent damage and misuse.

2. The idea for the key came from the Royal Association for Disability Rights (RADAR). The scheme began back in 1981 and is now often known as The National Key Scheme (NKS).

3. More than 9000 locked toilets in the UK can now be opened with a Radar key. Toilets fitted with a Radar key can now be found in pubs, cafés, department stores, shopping centres, bus and train stations and many other locations.

4. Radar keys are more than double the length of an average key (around 4 inches long) so that people with physical impairments, or who are physically frail, can still manage to use them.

How do I get a Radar key?

You might be able to get a free key from your local authority. If not, you could be asked to pay a small charge (around £5 including postage and package).

You can buy a key from Disability Rights UK www.disabilityrightsuk.org, or you may be able to buy one from your local social services department (it's usually best to contact the Adult Services team).

 Good to know

Worried about being able to find a disabled toilet? You can also get a list of available NKS toilets in your area (for a small donation of around £3.50) when you buy a Radar Key.

Going further...13 ways to make holidays happier if you have dementia

Fancy a holiday? Living with dementia can be stressful and isolating. If the condition is taking its toll on you both, physically and mentally, it might be time you both had a chance to relax and unwind. But holidays can be stressful too, can't they? Well yes, they can — but if you follow the tips below you could find ways to manage the stress.

Three golden rules

While you're planning and preparing for your trip it's very important to:

1. Be realistic — your loved one may have enjoyed month-long holidays in far flung locations before, but perhaps something short and simple and nearer home would be more suitable now?

2. Be honest — don't try to hide their condition when you're booking a holiday. Instead, explain the diagnosis and what it might involve to anyone who may need to know, including hotels and tour operators.

3. Be organised — you will be responsible for everything from travel documents and medication to sun cream and spending money.

Where will you stay?

Friend or family

Many people find this is a good choice. The person with dementia can spend time with loved ones they may not see very often, while also staying in an environment which is comfortable and welcoming. You can often hand over responsibility to others (at least for a few hours each day) and take some well-deserved 'me time.'

Tip: Pick a quiet time for travelling, avoiding school holidays or bank holidays if possible.

Package holiday

This can sound appealing, as accommodation, travel and meals are sorted for you before you leave. If the person with dementia is only mildly affected this kind of holiday could be a great success, particularly if you choose a location which is familiar to them or contains many happy memories.

Tip: Go out of season when resorts are quieter and airports are less busy (it's cheaper too).

Specialist holiday

You may find a holiday specially designed for people with dementia (and their carers) to be the least stressful option — and there are plenty to choose from. For example, if the person you're caring for is in the earlier stages of the dementia journey they may enjoy a more adventurous holiday, including activities such as sailing or walking. If their needs are more complex, you could choose a relaxing, pampering holiday with the option of extra nursing care if necessary.

Tip: These holidays can be expensive, so if you're struggling financially find out if you're entitled to respite care.

A DIY mini break

Of course you could organise your own break, either in the UK or abroad. This may offer more choice and flexibility than a package deal — and it could be cheaper, too.

Tip: Consider inviting someone else along to help you, otherwise you may find it isn't much of a holiday for you!

Your holiday checklist

Don't leave home without...

1. Insurance — pre-existing medical conditions, such as dementia, aren't normally covered in standard travel insurance so you may need to take out specialist insurance in case your loved one has an accident relating to their dementia. Take the insurance documents with you on holiday in case you need to make a claim (and always take your European Health Insurance Card).

2. All necessary medication and a doctor's letter explaining the dementia diagnosis and including any information about medication or treatments that may become necessary if your loved one becomes ill.

3. Making sure the person with dementia always has identification on them in case they become separated from you. You could also consider using a tracking device.

And don't forget

The chances of losing something tends to increase when you're with a person who has memory problems, so take extra care by:

- Making two lists of everything you've put in the suitcase and leave a duplicate list with someone else in case the one you're carrying goes missing.

- If you're taking passports, make two copies of the personal details page of each passport, take one copy with you (but keep it separate to the passports) and leave the other with someone at home.

- Take your sense of humour! If you can both laugh together you're far more likely to have a happy holiday. Enjoy your trip!

Chapter 6: Making every day count

The idea of 'living in the moment' is widely considered one of the best ways to approach dementia care. Focusing on the present, and making it as meaningful as possible, will bring your loved one enjoyment, and give you a sense of satisfaction. After all, none of us can control what will happen in the future but we can make the most of what we have right now.

The importance of creativity

Creative pastimes and hobbies are a great way to turn ordinary days into special ones. Here's a few ideas to inspire you.

Make a memoir — it's easier than you think

There's something very satisfying about recounting memorable moments from your life and collecting them together. So don't be daunted by the idea — you don't have to create a perfectly written memoir (although you can if you want to!). Working on your life story can simply mean collecting treasured items and keeping them in a shoe box (see below). Or your life story could be told entirely through photographs so that nobody needs to worry about grammar and punctuation!

Six reasons to create a life story

Working on their life story has many advantages for people with dementia;

1. It relieves boredom and feelings of isolation

2. It boosts self-esteem — being able to recall events in vivid detail will create a sense of pride and confidence.

3. Reminiscence is both enjoyable and stimulating.

4. It's an activity which has great meaning and purpose — their life story may never become a best seller but it will undoubtedly be treasured by loved ones and friends for years to come.

5. It can bring you closer together. Sharing the task of creating a life story means you have a common purpose — and you might even learn something you didn't know about your loved one.

6. Professional carers and care home staff find life story work extremely useful. It can speed up the 'getting to know you' process and provide a rich source of conversation.

Two warnings

Don't try to take over. It's the process of creating their story that matters more than the final product. Above all else, this is their life story so it must be personal.

Do show genuine interest and make an effort to really listen to what they're saying. Don't fake it — they might be able to detect insincerity and feel hurt.

Sources of inspiration

- Old photographs or mementos are probably the most obvious place to start. Everything from baby photos and christening shawls to more obscure photographs of great-great grandfather's old medals or faded certificates.

Tip: Write the names of people you don't know on the back of the photos, alongside a rough date of when it was taken...just in case you both forget later!

- Spread the net further. Is there a particular moment in their life that seems particularly vivid? Whether it's an event during World War II, the day they bought their first car, or a uniform they wore in their first job, you might be able to find more generic photographs or information online to trigger even more memories or create a theme.

- Go outside. Life story work doesn't have to take place indoors. Visiting a favourite place, a church they used to use, an area they used to live or work in, could also promote many happy memories and stories — as well as providing all the other benefits of getting out and about.

- Page by page. If you're aiming to create a life story book you'll need to have chapters which can be as simple as 'My childhood' or 'My working life' but can be more complex, incorporating any particular views or interests, if that's what they'd prefer.

Make a memory box

Your life story doesn't have to be written as a formal book. It could be stuck in a scrap book, or contained in a memory box.

Try covering a shoebox with paper or fabric that has special meaning or significance. Together, you can place mementos, photographs, ticket stubs, baby booties, a wedding tiara, or a first wage slip.

Rummaging inside the box and handling its content can bring great joy to a person with dementia. Memory boxes are also a very good way to stimulate conversation with visitors.

What about bad memories?

Sometimes painful and unhappy memories can emerge when someone with dementia is recalling the past. Don't panic if they start to cry or feel sad. You don't have to change the subject or try to cheer them up. Instead, simply stop what you're doing and listen until they've said all they need to. They may feel much better for having talked about it.

The power of music and art

One of the most difficult challenges for people living with dementia is being able to communicate how they feel. As the illness progresses, and words become more difficult to find, art and music can become very useful ways to ease this sense of frustration.

 Good to know

Research reveals that creative activities such as art and music promote the health and wellbeing of people with dementia because they;

• Stimulate curiosity

• Encourage self-expression

• Increase dignity and self-worth

Music

Many studies show that music can reduce agitation and ease challenging behaviour, providing a way to connect with the world even when verbal communication has become too difficult. Singing and music groups for people with dementia and their families are becoming increasingly popular and it's easy to see why.

It's a great confidence boost

Singing a song you learnt as a child is a source of delight for many people with dementia, particularly when they can remember all the words.

It's a sociable activity

Being part of a group can ease isolation and loneliness and provide a welcome distraction from daily routine.

It's a way to connect

Music is a very powerful emotional tool — a song can make anyone cry or laugh when it taps into a strong memory, and people with dementia are no exception.

Three ways to use music

1. Go out: Try an organised singing group such as Singing for the Brain, a service provided by the Alzheimer's Society which uses singing to bring people together in a friendly and stimulating social environment.

2. Make music at home: If you're not able to attend an organised group you can still incorporate a musical activity into your daily care plan. For example, encourage the person you're caring for to sing (use song books if necessary) clap, play a musical instrument, or dance (you could even join with them!)

3. Listen and enjoy: If they've moved into the later stages of the illness music can still bring a great deal of passive pleasure. For example, allow your loved one to choose the music themselves from a selection of their favourite music on CD or using a one button radio. Also try using music to create or enhance a mood — if you want them to feel relaxed chose something tranquil, if you want them to feel happy, try a favourite piece from childhood.

Art

Creating an art project can be totally absorbing for anyone. For someone with dementia, who may be feeling that they have little to offer anyone anymore, the process can be a way to restore dignity, ease anxiety, foster a sense of control and relieve boredom. And it doesn't seem to matter whether they've always been a keen artist or they haven't picked up a paint brush since childhood. Here's why:

It's a relaxing activity

People with dementia are often far calmer and happier after an art therapy session, and are less likely to become agitated.

It's a way to communicate

Everything from colour and brush choice to subject matter can reveal how someone is feeling at that moment — which is invaluable if the person you're caring for finds it difficult to talk much.

It opens the mind

Research suggests that artistic ability is often preserved in spite of the degeneration of the brain and the loss of more mundane day-to-day memory.

 Did you know?

Despite having a severe case of vascular dementia, internationally renowned sculptor Mary Hecht was able to draw detailed sketches and portraits all from memory in the years leading up to her death.

Three ways to use art

1. Go out — Join an organised art group. If necessary, ones for people with dementia are available at many day centres. Or contact Arts4Dementia (www.arts4dementia.org.uk) and find out what's happening in your area.

2. Make art at home — Lots of dementia specific products are slowly becoming available so that you can keep the subject matter adult if possible. If not, it might not matter very much providing you try not to patronise the person you're caring for and don't rush them to finish. Their art work doesn't have to be completed in one sitting.

Talk whilst you paint — encourage them to discuss what they're painting. If they need help, or a bit of assistance, then give it but don't take over. Remember, it's the process itself that matters — not the end product.

3. Visit art galleries — Looking at art, talking about it and appreciating it passively has been shown in research to have a positive effect on the cognitive ability of people with dementia — it's also very enjoyable and can help the person you're caring for stay active and feel involved with the outside world.

Some people with dementia seem perfectly content to sit around all day, but whilst some relaxation is always a good idea, so is some physical activity. It won't only improve their physical health (take a look at the benefits below) it will improve their mental health too.

Find a dementia friend

Everyone needs a friend but a dementia diagnosis can, sadly, bring a stigma with it which may mean that old friends start slipping away. However, this doesn't have to lead to social isolation and loneliness. In fact, if you take advantage of befriending schemes and support groups, you could both find yourselves forming new, long-lasting friendships.

Who are befrienders?

Befrienders are volunteers who've been trained in dementia and are genuinely interested in forming friendships with people who have the condition. Their interest often comes from personal experience — perhaps they've cared for a relative or friend with dementia in the past and have some understanding of the challenges it can bring. Befrienders are also able to provide companionship for carers who may be experiencing caregiver stress or depression and are in need of support themselves.

What do befrienders actually do?

- Befrienders are carefully matched to the people they befriend. They usually start by going to meet the person in their own home and getting to know them. A lot depends on whether or not they both hit it off. If not, that's fine — there'll be no hard feelings — the befriending service will simply try to find someone more suitable.

- If they do hit it off, then the befriender will start visiting regularly (perhaps once a week). At first, visits might simply involve chatting over a cup of tea, looking at photographs or listening to music. As their friendship builds, visits might involve going shopping, playing golf together or going on outings to favourite places. Since befriending is person-centred care it's usually left to the person with dementia to decide what will happen on each visit.

- Befriending schemes can bring far reaching benefits. A befriender can, for example, provide a great boost to confidence, self-esteem and independence. Befrienders can also help to ease boredom and loneliness and provide much needed stimulation.

How do we find a befriender?

Contact charities such as Age UK, the Royal Voluntary Service and the Alzheimer's Society to find out about the dementia befriending schemes they run throughout the UK. Some NHS trusts also run befriending schemes for people with dementia and their carers — get more information at your local GP practice.

Support groups for carers

Caring for someone with dementia can be frustrating and stressful, but many carers find that simply meeting other people who are doing the same sort of job, sharing information, and realising they are not alone, can be very beneficial. There are hundreds of support groups nationwide offering social, practical and emotional support for the carers, family and friends of people with dementia. Support groups can meet face-to-face or online.

 Good to know

Numerous studies have found 'statistically significant evidence' that peer support groups can be a positive benefit for carers of people with dementia.

Keep on moving — the importance of staying active when you have dementia

You probably already know that physical exercise is really good for people with dementia but one particular form of exercise has been found to increase their likelihood of remaining mobile and independent for longer. It's called strength-building exercise (sometimes known as resistance training) and the more they do of it, the better they could feel.

What is strength training?

Strength training is physical activity using weights or resistance — including your own body weight — to work muscles in the body. Muscle-strengthening activities can include climbing stairs, walking uphill, lifting or carrying shopping, digging the garden, or weight training.

Three reasons why strength building exercise is important

- It helps maintain strong muscles and flexible joints meaning people with dementia can continue to look after themselves.
- It reduces their risk of fracturing or breaking bones — which can be traumatic.
- It helps to improve their balance and coordination which can, in turn, prevent falls and other accidents.

 Did you know?

Research reveals that regular strength training exercises can improve daily activities such as climbing stairs, walking and moving around the house, getting up from a chair, bed or floor, and putting on socks. Improvements in such small tasks significantly improve the quality of life of people with Alzheimer's or dementia.

Three signs they aren't getting enough exercise

1. They've become more sedentary since being diagnosed.
2. They struggle to get up from a chair without help.
3. They're increasingly nervous about walking unaided or doing things for themselves.

How to get more strength building exercise into daily life

Strength training can be suitable for all levels of fitness and can be done at all stages of the dementia journey.

Swimming

Swimming is gentle on the joints so it's particularly good for people who suffer from arthritis. If your loved one used to enjoy swimming you could find that being in the water helps to reignite memories of swimming, combining physical activity with feel-good memories.

Pilates

Pilates builds strength and balance, improves posture and can reduce stress. Classes are also quite energetic and sociable so it definitely has all-round benefits for someone in the early stages of dementia.

Tip: Consider a Pilates DVD or book if you think a class could be too much for them to cope with.

Gardening

Gardening can increase strength and flexibility and help a person with dementia to stay fit and agile.

Housework

Vacuuming, walking up and down stairs and moving around the house can build strength and improve flexibility.

If the above suggestions might be too strenuous, encourage them to

- Stand up and move regularly — this will keep leg muscles stronger.
- Sit unsupported for a few minutes each day — this will strengthen the stomach and back muscles to support posture.
- Try some bicep curls (see below).

Step-by-step bicep curls

- Sit on a firm chair without arms (a dinning chair is ideal) and with feet flat on the floor.
- Hold light hand weights (or tins of baked beans from the cupboard) at the sides with arms straight and palms facing towards the body.
- Slowly bend one elbow lifting the weight towards the chest.
- Hold the position for up to 5 seconds and slowly lower the arm again.
- Repeat with the other arm.
- Continue until you've done 8–15 repetitions.

Your motivation check list

1. Is it enjoyable? Whatever strength-building exercise you do, it should be fun.
2. Is it a priority? Try to make some daily exercise as important as eating regular meals, not something you'll try to squeeze in if you have a few spare minutes.
3. Is there enough variety? If it gets boring, neither of you will want to do it.
4. Is it easy to fit in? This is crucial — if it's a hassle, you'll soon stop.

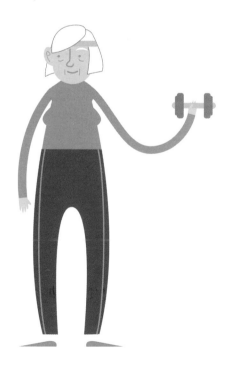

Benefits of moving more

1. It's good for your heart and can reduce high blood pressure.
2. It keeps your bones and muscles strong so you can stay mobile and independent.
3. It improves sleep.
4. It can reduce the risk of falls by improving strength and balance.
5. It improves confidence and reduces loneliness especially if it involves mixing with other people.
6. It might ease agitation, anxiety, restlessness and wandering.

Don't worry if your loved one is reluctant to do very much. Try to work out why. Maybe they've lost their confidence or are afraid they'll fall? Keep reassuring them that they're safe with you. If necessary try using a walking stick or rollator to provide extra comfort and safety, and if you're going outdoors make sure they're dressed properly so they stay warm and comfortable.

Three facts worth knowing

1. Tai Chi is often regarded as the perfect exercise for elderly people. Research has shown that older people who regularly perform the traditional Chinese art, were less likely to suffer high blood pressure and were physically stronger.
2. Gentle daily exercise — 30 minutes, six days a week — was found by researchers to be as good for elderly men as stopping smoking.
3. Regular exercise can boost the size of parts of the brain that shrink with age. If you're worried about your own memory, you might be able to reduce your risk of developing dementia by taking a brisk 30-40 minute walk three times a week.

Supervised swimming can also be a great work out and stress buster. So keep an open mind!

Golden rules

Keep it simple

Look at your daily care plan. Does it include something physical every day? It could be as simple as taking a 15 minute walk, or doing some housework or light gardening.

Make it fun

What did they used to enjoy doing? Whether it was dancing, swimming or walking, you might find it easier than you thought to take it up again. For example, you could make the most of afternoon tea dances in your area, they're not only sociable and fun but will increase strength and flexibility.

What if ...

They need more persuasion

Keep reminding the person with dementia of the benefits these simple exercises could bring. For example, 'Just a few minutes every day and you could feel stronger, have more energy and keep your independence.'

You're worried about money

Physical activity doesn't have to cost very much. A decent pair of shoes or trainers is all you need to go for a walk, and many local authorities run low-cost (or free) exercise and swimming sessions for older people. If cost is still an issue however, you could consider making any physical activity expense, part of your personal budget.

They're no longer mobile

Don't let that put you off. If the person you're caring for is wheelchair bound, or too frail to stand for very long, seated exercise programmes are widely available — from armchair aerobics on DVD, to seated dancing classes in your local community centre. Stay positive — you might be surprised by how much is available.

Chapter 7: All about you

Remember the oxygen mask theory? We've all listened to the safety talk on board a plane and been told to put on our own oxygen mask before trying to help anyone else. The same applies when you're caring for someone with dementia because if you don't look after your own health first, you will really struggle to look after theirs.

Here's how to keep yourself in good shape, physically and mentally

Staying healthy

You might be happy to devote yourself to a loved one with dementia but don't underestimate how tough caring can be on your own physical and mental health.

 Did you know?

65 per cent of older carers (aged 60–94) have health problems themselves.

Could this be you?

As a carer you always want to do your best and you know how important it is for you to stay in good shape BUT —

• Your loved one has to come first.

• If they need something done, you're usually the only person who can do it.

• You don't have the time or energy to think about yourself.

Carers can run into personal difficulties with everything from back problems to eating well, stress and depression. Try to avoid neglecting your own health because you 'don't have time' to look after yourself. This is a very common issue with carers and it doesn't help anyone in the long run so make sure you have some 'me time' every day — it isn't 'selfish' it's essential.

Besides, looking after your own health doesn't have to mean neglecting the person you're caring for. Here's how to make it happen:

Eat well

If you're already encouraging your loved one to eat a healthy diet it shouldn't be too difficult for you to do the same! Start with a filling, nutritious breakfast, eat regular healthy snacks — such as cereal bars, fruit and yoghurt — and go for Mediterranean-style main meals which are low on red meat but contain fish, lots of whole grains, vegetables, nuts and olive oil. Consider fresh meal delivery services if you're short on time.

Look after your back

Many carers find they develop back problems as a result of lifting, carrying and other physical tasks involved in looking after a person with dementia.

Have you been shown how to lift safely?

There are certain techniques you need to know which could make lifting easier or ask your GP, practice nurse or local carers group for as much advice and support as possible.

Have you had an assessment?

You may be entitled to extra practical help at certain times of the day or week, or financial help to make alterations to your home. Ask your GP to refer you to the local occupational therapy unit for assessment.

Are you standing tall?

Poor posture can put extra strain on your back and make back pain even worse, it can also cause muscle, joint and disc damage. So don't hunch your shoulders or slump in your chair. When you're standing, keep your back straight and your head facing forward.

Stay active

Yes, we know you're always on the go and are exhausted by the end of each day, but a small amount of the right kind of activity could actually increase your energy levels, improve your flexibility, lift your mood and make life easier to cope with.

Be realistic — A 15 minute walk is enough to get started — try to have one every day. If you can manage a swim, bike ride or a fitness/exercise class once or twice a week, that's great. Consider other activities too, such as yoga, Pilates or tai-chi which could also help you to relax.

Keep your appointments

It's all too easy for a carer to cancel a doctor's appointments because 'something came up' and their loved one needed them at home. However, this can be pretty dangerous and won't, in the long run, do the person you're caring for any favours either. After all, who will look after them if you get really ill and have to go into hospital? So make sure you attend all GP, nurse, hospital, dental, osteopathy and podiatry appointments, go for regular screening tests when you're invited, and consider taking a flu jab if you're offered one.

Tip: This is a necessity. The next time you're tempted to cancel an appointment, tell yourself, 'this is not a luxury, it is an absolute necessity.'

Listen to your body

Is there something you really need to sort out but keep putting off? A worrying lump, pain, headache, cough or bowel problem needs to be investigated — and the sooner the better.

Avoiding depression

Caring for a loved one with dementia can be emotionally draining so it's no wonder many carers feel down and have 'bad days' some of the time.

Could this be you?

You work hard and have always taken pride in caring for your loved one to the best of your ability BUT:

* You're beginning to feel that nothing you do is good enough.
* You are tired all the time, tearful or angry and easily agitated.
* You're suffering physical symptoms such as headaches, chronic pain or digestive problems that won't go away.

If you're feeling most of the symptoms above it's likely that you're depressed. But try not to worry, depression is not a sign of weakness, it's an understandable reaction to your current situation. In fact it's probably a testament of your strength that you've managed to keep caring for your loved one despite feeling so low. And the good news is that now you've recognised what's wrong, there's plenty you can do to feel better.

 Did you know?

Researchers have found that a person who provides care for someone with dementia is twice as likely to suffer from depression as a person providing care for someone without dementia.

You aren't alone

There are 670,000 people in the UK caring for a loved one with dementia and 40 per cent of them (almost 270,000 men and women) are clinically depressed or suffering from anxiety at any one time.

Why you might be feeling depressed

Caring for anyone is hard work — it's probably the hardest job you've ever done. But caring for a loved one with dementia, and making sure they're always safe, isn't only physically exhausting, it can be lonely and frustrating, too, and raises all kinds of personal and emotional issues. Watching someone you love deteriorate mentally, behave totally out of character, become aggressive, embarrassing, or hurtful is often described as a 'living grief.' It feels like the person you've known for a lifetime has disappeared...but you still love and have to care for the person they are now.

10 ways to help tackle depression

1. Go back to basics

Making sure you eat properly and look after your physical health might sound obvious, but it's surprising how many carers start neglecting their own basic needs. Remember, it's not selfish to spend time preparing a healthy meal or keep a doctor's appointment — it's essential.

2. Sort out your sleep

Sleep helps the brain and body recover from fatigue and a lack of sleep contributes to depression. If your loved one disturbs your sleep at night but has naps during the day, try doing the same (it's more important than household chores) or talk to someone you trust. If you have a community nurse, or other professional to confide in make use of them, because they may be able to suggest ways to help you both sleep better.

3. Take a good look at your bedroom

Make sure your mattress and pillow are comfortable, your bedroom is dark enough and isn't too hot or too cold. If you have cold feet try wearing socks to bed. Your body needs to regulate your temperature before you can go to sleep.

4. Consider complimentary therapies

Many people with mild insomnia swear by herbal remedies such as valerian, lavender and camomile, although scientific evidence is limited. Acupuncture, hypnotherapy, and reflexology can also aid relaxation and encourage restful sleep.

 Did you know?

Science backs up the old theory that a warm milky drink eases insomnia and restlessness, because calcium can reduce muscle spasms and soothe tension.

5. Keep a journal

Write in it every day and express all the emotions you're feeling such as fear, pain or anger. Unleashing it all could really help to improve your mood. Looking back over it in the future might also help you cope with the emotional roller coaster.

6. Take time out

Scheduling in regular 'me time' is crucial and it isn't selfish. Spending time doing something you enjoy every day (whether it's having a bath, doing a crossword, or watching your favourite soap) won't only make you feel better, it will make you a better carer.

7. Get outside

Outdoor exercise is as effective as antidepressants in treating mild to moderate depression, and research shows that contact with nature and green spaces can significantly reduce stress levels, enhance your mood and also boost your heart health. Go for a walk in a park, help a friend on their allotment, plant sunflower seeds in your garden — and get your loved one to help you if they want to.

8. Try to stay positive

Having a positive attitude has been scientifically proven to combat anxiety and depression and improve your health. Remind yourself every day of the successes you've had, the rewards of caring and the satisfaction it has often brought you. Positive thinking has health benefits too. Optimists have stronger immune systems and are able to fight off bugs, viruses, disease and recover more quickly from operations.

9. Phone a friend

Arrange to meet a fellow carer once a week for a coffee and a 'reality chat.' This means that once you've poured your heart out to them, you then ask them to put what you've said into perspective, and remind you of the positives, too. This will be far more constructive than simply sounding off.

10. Know when it's time to ask for professional help

If the self-help tips above don't seem to be making much difference, then it could be time to get professional help. After all, depression deserves to be treated like any other illness. Your GP should be able to offer you everything from anti-depressant medication to psychological therapies such as Cognitive Behavioural Therapy (CBT), and Mindfulness-based Cognitive Therapy (MBCT), which is now recommended by the National Institute for Clinical Excellence (NICE) for the treatment of depression. Sometimes a combination of medication and talking therapies works best.

 Good to know

A recent study revealed that eight sessions of psychological therapy could reduce anxiety and depression in people caring for a loved one with dementia.

10 symptoms of caregiver stress — and how to beat them

There's no denying that caring for a loved one with dementia can be very stressful, but whilst some stress is normal and manageable, if you regularly feel overwhelmed you could be heading for burnout. Here's how to spot the signs...

Could this be you?

Take a look at the statements below:

1. You can't sleep properly (even when your loved one does).

2. You're permanently exhausted and can't be bothered to do things you used to enjoy.

3. You suffer stomach complaints, headaches or have other aches and pains you can't seem to shift.

4. You get angry and snappy with your loved one when they repeat themselves or behave in a way that you know they can't help.

5. You worry constantly about money, future finances and how you'll be able to manage.

6. You've lost your appetite and aren't eating properly — or are eating too much and have gained weight.

7. You're having anxiety or panic attacks.

8. You're drinking or smoking too much.

9. You pretend everything's fine and rarely ask for help.

10. You often feel tearful and emotional when you think about 'what might have been' if your loved one hadn't been diagnosed with dementia.

Now be honest with yourself. How many of these statements sound familiar? Do you recognise yourself in quite a few of them? Remember, stress doesn't only affect you mentally, it can lead to physical ill health which, in turn, can impact on your ability to be a good carer.

So even if you find it hard to put yourself first (many carer's do), if you're determined to do the best you can for your loved one, you need to start taking care of yourself, too.

Here's how:

1. Have a carer's assessment

Your local social services department might be able to offer you help with day to day caring, or provide you with equipment to make life easier. But first, you have to be assessed by them. So phone them today and ask if you can have a carer's assessment. Even if you aren't entitled to free help, they might be able to suggest other ways of getting support so it's definitely worth doing.

2. Lower your expectations

Many carers simply expect too much of themselves. Take a look at your daily care plan and ask yourself if it can be modified. Do you really need to drive to a local beauty spot for a walk when the park is far nearer? Does every meal have to be cooked from scratch? If many of your efforts seem to go unnoticed and unappreciated, they might be creating more stress than they are actually worth.

3. Learn more about dementia

Repetitive behaviour can be incredibly difficult to deal with on a daily basis but understanding why it's happening, can make it more manageable. The same applies to challenging behaviour such as aggression, and awkward questions. The more knowledge you have about the different approaches to dementia care the less helpless you'll feel.

4. Take a break

Okay, so this does sound pretty obvious but it's amazing how many carers neglect themselves and their need for 'me time.' Are you always coming up with excuses as to why you can't take a few hours off? Do you think respite care will be too difficult to manage or your loved one might refuse to go anywhere without you — even a day centre? Try to keep an open mind, you could be pleasantly surprised.

5. Learn to relax

Many carers say they've 'forgotten' how to relax and with so many demands on their time it's easy to see why. But just about everyone can manage to put aside 10 minutes every day to listen to a relaxation CD. Perhaps you and the person you're caring for could do something together. A yoga or Pilates DVD might help you both to feel calmer.

6. Have a health check

It's sadly common for carers to neglect their own health and skip doctor's appointments because they don't have time, or cancel them because the person they're caring for is having a bad day. As a result, minor ailments can become major ones. Even if you don't feel particularly unwell but haven't seen a doctor for years, it's worth making an appointment for a general health check. Most GPs offer midlife health MOTs every five years for people aged 40–74.

7. Spiritual support

Are you neglecting your faith? Perhaps you're struggling to make sense of your loved one's diagnosis. If so, you might find solace in your religion, or in a new spiritual belief. Don't discount the help you may be able to get from your vicar, rabbi, priest, imam, or spiritual advisor.

8. Counselling

Dementia carers are unfortunately at high risk of depression but the good news is there are lots of ways to get help. Start by asking your GP to refer you for counselling on the NHS. You can sometimes refer yourself — pick up a leaflet about Talking Therapies at your local GP practice.

9. Change your mind

It can be hard to think positively when life feels such a daily struggle, but the age-old practise of 'counting your blessings' can help put even the bleakest most stressful day into perspective. Try to find at least three things to be grateful for each day. It can be as simple as a sunny afternoon, a smile from your loved one, or a perfect cup of tea. Get in the habit of writing them down each day, or download a free gratitude journal app on your phone (there are hundreds to choose from). The more you do it, the easier it gets and the better you'll feel.

10. Get support from your peers

It's all very well being told how to beat stress from other well-meaning friends and experts, but nothing beats confiding in someone who really knows what you're going through... because they're going through it too. Support groups whether face to face or online are invaluable because, although everyone's dementia journey is unique, you might be comforted to find similarities in experiences, and heartened by tips and advice others can offer.

Making Time for You

It's all too easy to forget about yourself when you're caring for someone with dementia.

Could this be you?

You know it would do you good to take time off and put your own needs first occasionally but:

- You really don't have the time.
- It's a bit selfish and you'd feel guilty.
- You can manage without it.

Here's why it isn't selfish and you can't manage without some 'me time':

You do a very difficult job

Many carers feel overwhelmed, lonely and frustrated, as a result they can start to neglect their own health and become physically ill, reducing their ability to care and often resulting in their loved one prematurely going into a care home.

You need to take control

When your time is spent caring for someone else, it's easy to start feeling that they — not you — are in control of your life. This is another reason why carers can feel 'helpless' and become depressed.

It will make you a better carer

Having a chance to rest, relax, enjoy yourself and recharge your batteries won't only help to boost your mood, it could improve the way you do your job. Many carers say they come back to their work with renewed vigour and a clearer perspective on how to deal with challenges and difficult behaviour.

It could help your loved one

You may find this hard to believe, but the person you're caring for might also enjoy a break from you! Having the company of others can help relieve boredom and loneliness and provide extra stimulation, particularly if it involves them going to a day centre or joining a social group.

How to make it happen

Schedule it in

You need to consider 'me time' to be just as important as the other regular activities you do with the person you care for. So take a look at your daily care plan and find a way to incorporate at least 15 minutes every day for yourself.

Daily 'me time' could be having a coffee and reading a newspaper, soaking in a bubble bath, doing a crossword or painting your nails at the end of the day.

Make a list

If you're struggling to think of anything you could do with your 'me time' it could mean you've got out of the habit of thinking about yourself (many carers do). So make a list of simple things you enjoy doing and that make you happy. From buying yourself a bunch of flowers, to watching tennis on TV or reading a thriller.

Ask for help

Be honest with friends and family and explain that any help (even 30 minutes so you could go for a walk on your own) would be appreciated. You might be surprised by how easily they come on board.

When was your last carer's assessment? If the person you're looking after now has greater needs you might be entitled to extra help or short-term respite care. NHS respite care is free so start by going to your GP. You could also check out what help is available from local day care centres, or from charity befriender schemes. You may even be able to get financial help towards a holiday for yourself or for both of you.

Time to take a break

Could this be you?

You're worn out and you know you should take some time off from caring but:

- Your loved one might become very upset if you're not there.
- You'd worry too much to enjoy yourself.
- Money is tight, you simply can't afford it.

Caring is hard enough without feeling you can't ever have a rest. So whether you'd like a couple of hours, or a couple of weeks to yourself, find out what to do if you need respite care.

Ask for a carer's assessment

These are often done at the same time as a care needs assessment and help to identify what support you both need on the dementia journey. These assessments should also reveal if you are entitled to financial help, which can include funding for respite care.

 **Did you know?**

Some respite care is free but it's often means-tested and the person with dementia could have to make some sort of contribution towards it.

Funding for respite care

The Care Act 2014 makes it clear that if anyone does have to pay for respite care it should be the person with dementia (not the carer) but that they should only be charged a 'reasonable amount.'

But even if you know you aren't eligible for financial help, it's still worth having a carer's assessment because it could provide you with all sorts of information about respite care and the choices available in your area. So if you haven't had a carer's assessment (or haven't had one recently and feel you now need more help) contact your local social services department to arrange one.

Two types of respite care

1. Your loved one can be cared for at home by a professional carer (funded by the council if you are eligible) whilst you go out for a few hours, or even take a holiday.
2. They could go to a residential care home for a short stay.

Warning: Although most carers prefer the idea of their loved one staying at home, rather than being moved somewhere new for a short while, this might not be feasible, especially if they have complex care needs which you — or your local authority — can't afford to fund. So try to keep an open mind. Your loved one might actually enjoy the stimulation of a new environment, even if it is only temporary.

What happens if you have no funding, and no money?

If for some reason you aren't able to get your break funding and can't afford to pay for it yourself don't give up. Here's a few more ideas you could try.

Friends and family

Could the person you're caring for go to stay with someone else for a few days? Or could they come to stay in your home so you can take a break? Remember, it isn't selfish to ask for help, it's essential for your physical and mental health. Besides, your loved one might need a break from you as well!

Little and often

If a week's holiday or an overnight stay is too complicated or expensive to arrange, could short, regular breaks be worth considering? Take a look at local day centres and activities for people with dementia and remember all the people who offered help when your loved one was first diagnosed.

You may not have seen some of them recently — dementia does, sadly, still carry a stigma — but you might be pleasantly surprised by how many of them would still be happy to offer you practical help.

Carer check list

- Are you receiving all the benefits, grants or help from outside agencies, such as community nurses that you might be entitled to?

- Do you have your own support network? Meeting or talking to other carers who have some idea what you're going through can be invaluable.

- Are you going out enough? Getting outside is good for you and your loved one. Whether it's just a walk around a park or a trip to the local shops, aim to go out as often as you can.

- Is it time to stop? Caring for someone with dementia can be so difficult that nobody could possibly blame you if, at some point, you have to hand over to someone else, or start looking at care homes. This can be a very difficult decision for any carer, but it's an important one to consider, particularly in the later stages of dementia when you might simply have to accept that your loved one needs more day-to-day assistance than you can offer, and it might be best for them — and for you — if you start to let go.

 Good to know

US research reveals that respite care doesn't only ease stress and depression in family carers, it can improve the relationship between the carer and the person with dementia, while a study by researchers at Utah State University revealed that carers who look after their own mental health provide better care for their loved ones with dementia and can potentially slow down the progress of their illness by as much as 37 per cent.

Chapter 8: Planning, preparing and learning to let go

No matter how well you care for a person with dementia or how much you love them, at some point their dementia journey will reach its end. Whilst this may be very painful to consider, if you spend a little time planning and preparing now, you could save yourself a lot of heartache, regret and confusion.

 Did you know?

On average, a person diagnosed with Alzheimer's disease will live for another 10-12 years, and many of those years can be made happy and enjoyable.

The legal stuff: What you need to know

Thinking ahead might seem depressing, but it's actually the best way to protect the person you're caring for and make sure they stay in control of their lives and medical care for as long as possible.

There are two types of power of attorney

- Health and welfare lasting power of attorney

This document allows the people appointed to make decisions about medical care, treatment and where the person with dementia should live. For example, whether it's best for a loved one to be looked after in a care home and whether they should be given life-prolonging treatment, such as resuscitation after a heart attack.

- Property and financial affairs lasting power of attorney

This document allows the people appointed to make decisions about money or property.

What is the process to set up Lasting Power of Attorney?

You'll need to download a special form to get things started with an LPA. These can be obtained from the government website https://yougov.co.uk.

Once all the relevant people have signed the form (and in a specific order), it must be sent off to The Office of the Public Guardian, which is part of the government's Justice Department. They handle all issues surrounding Lasting Power of Attorney. You'll need to also pay a fee when setting up the LPA.

Bear in mind that there is a slightly different process for applications made in Scotland and Northern Ireland.

What happens if we don't set up a Lasting Power of Attorney?

If you don't get round to setting up an LPA and your loved one becomes unable to make their own decisions, (the legal term for this is 'lacking capacity') a legal body called the Court of Protection will act on your behalf until someone can apply to them to become your Deputy (which is a bit like an attorney). Unfortunately, this process can be a lot more time consuming and expensive than setting up an LPA, so it's best to get organised as soon as possible and appoint your attorney now.

A Living Will

A living will is a way for your loved one to express thoughts, feelings and decisions about any care or treatment they might need in the future.

There are two types of living wills

1. An advanced statement

This is a document stating general wishes and views about the way your loved one wants to be cared for. It might discuss for example a desire to stay at home as long as possible, and can include non-medical issues too, such as whether they prefer a bath or shower. It's important to remember that *this isn't legally binding* but should always be taken into account by the people involved in their care.

2. An advanced decision (sometimes called an advanced directive)

If they are sure that, further down the line, they will want to refuse specific medical treatment (even treatment which might prolong life) this can be made clear in a document called an advanced decision. *This is a legally binding* document and it will take precedent over any decision made by a medical professional, carer or relative.

Why set up an advanced decision?

An advanced decision isn't only used by people living with dementia, it's for anyone who might, during the course of their illness, find it difficult or impossible to communicate their wishes. In legal terms this is known as lacking 'mental capacity'. An advanced decision gives you a legal right to decide now, while you still can, to refuse certain treatments in the future. For example, cardiopulmonary resuscitation (CPR), intensive care treatment, blood transfusions (this may be the case if your religion doesn't permit them) or antibiotics and intravenous fluids.

An advanced decision differs from the health and welfare lasting power of attorney because it is the person with dementia is making the decision about your health rather than their appointed attorney.

Tip: You can download ready-printed advanced decision documents from websites such as the Alzheimer's Society.

Do Not Attempt Resuscitation order (DNAR)

A DNAR is a very personal decision, which means your loved one has stipulated that they do not want to have cardio pulmonary resuscitation (CPR). Most people sign a Do Not Resuscitate form (DNAR) because they are already very unwell, and have decided that, should something serious happen, they'd rather let nature take its course.

BUT — a person with dementia might want to set up a DNAR before becoming ill, so that they can make sure their wishes are known well in advance.

Why have a DNAR?

Cardio pulmonary resuscitation (CPR) can be quite brutal for anyone who is already frail and can sometimes result in broken ribs and organ damage. Research also suggests that it only has a 10–15 per cent success rate.

Much like an Advanced Decision (see above) it is a legally binding document, but only covers resuscitation, and does not prevent other medical treatments in the way that an Advanced Decision does. Medical professionals will still provide treatment including making sure that your loved one is comfortable.

How do you set up a DNAR?

First port of call is undoubtedly a GP. He'll be able to discuss the order, what it involves and make sure that the person with dementia understands exactly what will happen if they decide to sign one.

The form will need to include the following information:

1. Your loved one's name, address, date of birth and NHS number.

2. The name, address and contact number of your GP.

3. A statement as to why CPR should not happen. The doctor will include one or more of the following statements:

- *Attempting CPR is unlikely to restart the patient's heart and breathing.*

- *No benefit will be gained from restarting the patient's heart and breathing.*

- *The expected benefit of the treatment is outweighed by the burdens and would not be in the best interests of the patient.*

- *Attempted resuscitation is against the competent patient's expressed wishes.*

Who needs to know about the form?

The following people need to know about the existence of the DNAR form:

- Their local GP (if they don't know already)

- The local ambulance service

- Consultants in hospital

- The out-of-hours doctor service

- Friends, family and carers

The BIG question: Is it time for residential care?

You may hate the idea of handing over the care of your loved one to someone else, but sometimes it can be for the best. Find out why it might happen and how to cope with feelings of guilt.

Could this be you?

You know how much the person you're caring for wants to stay at home and you've tried your very best to respect their wishes, BUT:

- Their behaviour is becoming very difficult to deal with.
- You don't think they're safe enough at home.
- You are physically and mentally exhausted.

It can be incredibly difficult to accept that a loved one needs more care than you can give. But since dementia usually does get worse in time, the sad truth is that the majority of families and carers reach a similar point on the dementia journey. Here are the main reasons why it might happen:

They're admitted to hospital

Accidents and falls do happen, even when you've done your very best to prevent them. People with dementia often have other medical conditions too such as heart disease or diabetes. If they have vascular dementia they are also more likely to suffer a stroke and need hospital treatment. Sadly, being in hospital can make them more confused, less independent and more likely to need residential care. And the longer they stay in hospital, the more likely this becomes.

Two facts worth knowing

- More than one third of people with dementia who go into hospital from their own home, go into a care home after being discharged.
- Falls, broken/fractured hips, urine infections, chest infections and strokes are the main reasons people with dementia are admitted to hospital.

They're very prone to wandering

If they keep going out and getting lost, or constantly wander off when you go out with them, you might be very worried they're going to get hurt. People with dementia are very vulnerable physically and mentally, and whilst there are ways to understand and cope with wandering you might not be able to prevent it happening, and feel they'd be better off in a safer environment where they'll be constantly monitored.

 Good to know

You may want to look into whether using a GPS location tracker could help tackle issues surrounding wandering. Many can be fitted to belts or on special wristbands so you can find out where someone is if they suddenly go missing.

They're becoming angry or aggressive

This can be one of the toughest challenges of caring for a loved one with dementia, particularly if their anger or aggression seems to be directed at you, the person who loves them most. You might find you can deal with some aspects of difficult behaviour but if you find yourself in physical danger, it may well be time to consider residential care.

They have a 'near miss'

Sometimes it takes a near disaster for family carers to accept they need to start looking at other living arrangements. For example, perhaps the person with dementia almost started a fire, or nearly fell down the stairs. If you've already made the home dementia-friendly as possible it's likely you'll decide to look at alternatives.

You can't cope anymore

Don't forget that caring for a loved one with dementia is one of the most difficult jobs you can do. Caregiver stress and depression (see chapter seven) are common side effects, and if you're not young yourself, it might seriously affect your own health, too. There's no shame in accepting your loved one now needs more care than you can provide.

 Good to know

- Handing over some of the day-to-day care to a professional, could help your relationship rather than hinder it. Instead of being a nurse/carer you can go back to being their wife/partner/son/daughter — and enjoy some quality time with each other.

- You might be pleasantly surprised. More and more care homes are gearing up to the needs of people with dementia and can be very welcoming, homely places. Or you may find other choices available to you, such as assisted living or sheltered accommodation.

Feeling guilty?

Don't worry, this is a decision which can leave everyone feeling sad and guilty. But try asking yourself what your loved one would say to you if they didn't have dementia. Would they say; 'I want you to keep worrying and wearing yourself out so that I can stay at home,' or would they say; 'You've done enough for me, and I want you to be happy, too.'

Two facts worth knowing

- Around 322,000 people with dementia live in care homes — that's one third of people with dementia.
- Around 80 per cent of care home residents have some form of memory problem.

End of life care: What you need to know

Dementia is not a terminal illness but it does tend to shorten lives. As difficult as this may be to accept, many people do find the final stage of the illness easier to handle if they are prepared and can do their best to allow a loved one to experience a peaceful and dignified death.

Why it's good to talk about the end

You might not want to talk about death or dying, particularly while you're loved one is still well. But having the chance to let other people know their final wishes can give someone with dementia a sense of freedom and control, as well as providing peace of mind. Many people with dementia also worry about becoming a burden to their family, so knowing that things are taken care of can be a weight off their mind.

Getting started

When the end comes most people have quite simple requests; they want to die with dignity, without pain, in familiar surroundings and with loved ones around them. So there's no harm in asking the person you're caring for if this is what they would envisage for themselves, too.

Getting clearer

Once you've got the conversation going, you can ask more probing questions. Areas to discuss could include, for example, whether they'd like to be at home (some people have very strong feelings about this) or wouldn't mind moving to a care home, providing it's comfortable, pleasant and the staff are compassionate. They might also have strong preferences about who they want to be with them — and who they don't want to be there! Far from being depressing, this kind of discussion can actually be quite a relief for someone with dementia. So listen carefully and assure them that you will respect their wishes.

Medical treatment

There's a strong chance your loved one won't actually die from dementia, but from a related condition such as a stroke, heart attack, or pneumonia. For this reason their treatment needs can often become quite complex. Legal areas to discuss include appointing attorneys, whether they'd like to consider having a DNAR (a Do Not Attempt Resuscitation Order) or write a living will (see above).

Spiritual requests

Religious or spiritual beliefs can provide great comfort to someone who is nearing the end of their life. Would they like a religious leader to visit or say special prayers? Again, this can be very personal, as some people find a visit from the clergy frightening when they're ill, whilst others welcome it whole-heartedly.

Good to know

Government guidelines on end of life care make it very clear that comfort and quality of life should be the priority, regardless of any medical complexity, and that all care — whether in a hospital, care home or at home — should be person centred. So reassure your loved one that their views and feelings will always be heard and will take precedent wherever possible.

Tip: Use kind, comforting phrases because this can, understandably, be an upsetting subject to broach. For example, try; 'You can always revisit things, but because you've done the first step it will be a bit easier.' Or 'You don't need to be frightened, it's much easier to do this earlier, now we can focus on enjoying life.'

Tip: If you're loved one has refused to discuss this subject with you, it's worth asking other friends and family if they've mentioned anything to them. Sometimes people with dementia don't want to share this kind of information with their children or younger relatives, but will talk about it with friends and peers.

What are the warning signs that life is nearing an end?

Generally speaking, as your loved one reaches the end of their life the symptoms of dementia may become increasingly pronounced.

For example, you may notice:

- Difficulties eating and swallowing
- Double incontinence
- Little or no speech
- Limited mobility — they may be bed bound

However, these symptoms don't necessarily mean that death is imminent. Some people can live with these symptoms for weeks or even months. It's also important to remember that people with dementia don't always die from dementia. In fact, around two thirds die from pneumonia.

Why does this happen?

As they become increasingly frail — physically and mentally — you may find that your loved one succumbs more easily to infections, or is more likely to have a fall or accident which leads to a hospital stay and can, in turn, cause further decline until they become very weak.

Signs that death may be very close include:

- Irregular 'stop start' breathing
- Inability to swallow
- Cold hands and feet
- Agitation or restlessness
- Drifting into unconsciousness

You aren't alone

Watching a loved one die is undoubtedly painful and harrowing, however you should both receive support from professionals. Whether the person with dementia is at home or in a care home or hospice, they should, according to government guidelines, receive care which manages their pain and symptoms and provides 'psychological, spiritual and social support.'

What you can expect

Nursing

If your loved one is at home, they should have regular visits from their GP and nursing care from a community nurse or nurse skilled in palliative care. Carers might also be available, particularly during the night so that you can get some rest yourself.

Equipment

Palliative nursing often requires special equipment which should be provided free of charge, such as special hospital-like beds and commodes.

Medication

A wide range of painkilling medication is available to people in the last days of life, to make sure they are as comfortable as possible. If they have difficulty swallowing, medication can be given as an injection or as patches which are absorbed through the skin.

But what if they are in pain?

For loved ones, this is usually the biggest worry of all, especially if the person with dementia can no longer talk or communicate. However there are still several ways to work out if they are experiencing any pain or discomfort.

For example,

- Do they look sweaty or pale?
- Are they grimacing or pulling faces
- Do they seem tense or unable to sleep?
- Are they moaning or shouting?

If you notice any of these symptoms — or something similar — make sure you let their nurse or doctor know, as stronger medication may be necessary.

Letting go

If you've been their main carer for a long time, it might seem strange to suddenly have professionals taking over. Maybe you don't know what to do or how to behave?

Here are a few ideas:

1. Sit quietly with your loved one. Just being there at the bedside can be very peaceful and you don't have to talk all the time.
2. If they're awake, do they have something pleasant to look at? Can they see the garden, favourite photograph or painting, or a flower arrangement?
3. Make sure their room has soft lighting and have some favourite calming music playing quietly in the background. Arrange a visit from a spiritual advisor or member of the clergy, if you feel it would bring comfort.
4. Hold their hand. Gentle touch can provide great comfort, even if they don't seem to be aware of it.

 Good to know

Caring for someone in the final hours of their life is often a very intense and intimate experience which allows a carer to feel close and connected to their loved one. Helping a person with dementia to experience a 'good' death may be, after all, the final gift you give them. Many carers say that knowing they did their best, right to the end, brought considerable comfort in the months ahead.

Words of inspiration

"Never believe that a few caring people can't change the world. For indeed, that's all who ever have."
Margaret Mead, author

"Too often we underestimate the power of a touch, a smile, a kind word or the smallest act of caring, all of which have the power to turn a life around."
Leo Buscaglia, author and motivational speaker

"To care for those who once cared for us is one of the highest honours."
Tia Walker, author and blogger

"Spending time with people who have dementia has made me a more patient parent, friend, daughter, sister and wife."
Anne Davis Basting, director of the Centre on Age and Community at the University of Wisconsin, Milwaukee

"Dementia caregivers are some of the best inventors, possess some of the most creative minds on the planet. They don't have the luxury of living in past successes. The scope of their work changes by the hour, their goals by the minute. They must constantly formulate new ideas and discover new solutions."
Mara Botonis, author

"One person caring about another represents life's greatest value."
Jim Rohn, entrepreneur, author and motivational speaker

"Someday those who care for a person with Alzheimer's may be faced with what appears to be an insoluble problem. Caregivers may try anything they have been taught but nothing works. So, they touch the arm of the person with Alzheimer's and speak softly and gently. Because of the patient's apparent distress, the caregiver may hug the person or give a kiss and the person that he or she is loved. One day, if the caregiver is lucky, a revelation occurs. That person learns that the last thing we ever lose is love. Our memories may be gone. Intellect and logic may have diminished. We may have forgotten your name and where we are or what we are doing. But we remember love."
Tim Brennan, poet

unforgettable

products | advice | community | services

· ·

At Unforgettable we bring together life-changing products, services and advice to help people with dementia do the things we take for granted.

Founded by James Ashwell after caring for his mother, we work with inventors, researchers, care homes, therapists and carers to find inn vative solutions for you.

It's our aim as a B Corp to create positive social impact by using business as a force for good. This is why we created the Unforgettable Foundation and why we work in partnership with leading dementia charities in the UK and internationally.

Visit www.unforgettable.org/charity-partners

We would love to hear from you so please do get in touch at **happytohelp@unforgettable.org** or on the phone **020 3322 9070.**

Why is an LPA important for us all?

It's an unfortunate truth that any of us could lose our mental capacity at any time due to accident or illness. With one in three of the over-65s being diagnosed with dementia at some point, we wanted to help, as this area is often overlooked and misunderstood.

Without a Lasting Power of Attorney in place your family members will not be able to easily manage your financial or welfare needs, so it is critical to put one in place. Some would say it's as critical as having a Will.

How can Unforgettable help?

Our services have been designed in collaboration with expert legal partners to help you through the process, offering you a simple and free questionnaire that completes your forms. Currently our service only covers England and Wales as there is a different process in Scotland and Northern Ireland.

Together we also provide a range of checking and drafting services to offer you peace of mind before registering with the Office of the Public Guardian. We've even introduced a dementia specific statement of wishes which helps address some important questions that aren't covered by the standard form.

You can find our more about these services on the following pages, by visiting our website, or by calling us on **020 3322 9070.**

Need more advice? Visit our website and sign up for our free eBook.

Everything you need to know. We've done the hard work for you. Our free guide cuts through the legal jargon with helpful information and advice on:

- Why get a Lasting Power of Attorney?
- How to fill out and register forms
- How to pick your attorneys
- How to use a Lasting Power of Attorney
- What is mental capacity?

Why choose the Unforgettable LPA service?

1. Free online service with great value support packages

No need to use expensive lawyers, our online service is free and for reassurance you can upgrade with our checking and drafting packages.

2. Faster, easier and secure

Simply answer our online questionnaire to automatically complete your forms.

3. Peace of mind checking service from only £89

Don't be one of 10% of registrations rejected by the Offi e of the Public Guardian every day. We can double check your forms.

4. Complete your LPA's over the phone from only £180

If you prefer not to do everything yourself, our experts can do it for you over the phone.

5. Our services are Dementia friendly with specific consideration for challenges relating to dementia and memory loss.

6. Get extra protection with Mental Capacity Certification

If you are concerned that mental capacity is in question our experts can visit you at home to provide, if appropriate, official m ntal capacity certifi ation.

7. Remember you don't need to be diagnosed with dementia to use our service.

It is open to anyone who wants to plan ahead for illness or accidents which can affect mental capacity.

8. Designed by Unforgettable and delivered by experts, Brook Worthy Law and Net Lawman.

Other helpful guides from Unforgettable

A trip to hospital is never easy. With dementia, the experience can be disorientating and traumatic. That's why we have worked with Danielle Wilde on a book to help you understand what you can do to reduce the risk of someone you know being admitted to hospital.

Common Causes:

- Falls
- UTI Infections
- Delirium
- Dehydration
- Aggression
- Pneumonia

The Book to help:

- What to look out for
- What to do next
- Tips and tricks to keep your loved ones safer and healthier
- Support advice and resources
- Many more ideas and products that could help

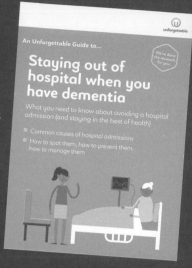

Description:

Written by Danielle Wilde, dementia lead at the Royal Free Hospital London NHS Foundation Trust. This book is for people caring for those with dementia and helps you identify, prevent and manage the common causes of hospital admissions.

Visit www.unforgettable.org/dementia-books

Introducing our new range of helpful eBooks.

Visit **www.unforgettable.org/E-Books** for more information

Other titles coming soon.

- Dementia Explained
- The Unforgettable Gift Guide
- A Guide to the Dementia Journey

Sign up to our newsletter to be notified about these exciting new releases and receive a free chapter from Dementia Explained!

Tell us what you think and get involved

We hope you found this book useful and that it makes a real difference. We set up Unforgettable to help people with dementia enjoy the best life possible. Help us be better! Give us your feedback on the things you read here. Things you found useful, that you particularly like or that you disagreed with.

Your ideas could help others!

We are trying to building a community of carers so that we can all learn from each other.

- Share your feedback
- Tell us your stories, tips and experiences
- Tell us about your product ideas or wishes
- Give us input on this book or any of our others

Get in touch

We are always happy to help, recommend products and to hear feedback and ideas, so please do get in touch or join our forum:

Web   www.unforgettable.org

Email   happytohelp@unforgettable.org

Phone 020 3322 9070

𝕏   @Unforget_org

   unforgettable.org

Some products and services that might help

The dementia journey is full of challenges which can feel overwhelming at times. If you're struggling right now, Unforgettable might be able to help. We have a wide range of products and services designed to make your life a little bit easier; from dealing with legal matters to finding practical ways to cope with incontinence or disrupted sleep. The next few pages offer a glimpse of what Unforgettable can do for you. Remember, you aren't alone.

Best wishes,

The Unforgettable team.

unforgettable

life-changing dementia products

We have over 1,000 life-changing products available online and a selection of our best-sellers available in selected LloydsPharmacy stores